Jambo

Durrell Wildlife Conservation Trust

Durrell Wildlife Conservation Trust was founded by the author and naturalist Gerald Durrell over forty years ago, with the mission to save species from extinction, and the trust has a proven track record of doing just that. Species that have been pulled back from the brink include the Mauritius kestrel, pink pigeon, echo parakeet and Mallorcan midwife toad, and our dedicated conservationists are hard at work in threatened habitats around the world, continuing the battle to protect and conserve many more.

With its international headquarters in Jersey, the trust has built up a worldwide reputation for its pioneering conservation techniques, developed under the leadership of Gerald Durrell. Today, Durrell Wildlife Conservation Trust is continuing to develop its overseas work in new areas of the world, with a particular focus on vulnerable communities of endemic animals, which make such a valuable contribution to global biodiversity.

Please don't let your interest in conservation end when you turn this page. Write to us now and we'll tell you how you can be part of our crusade to save animals from extinction.

For further information, or to send a donation, write to:

Durrell Wildlife Conservation Trust
Les Augrès Manor
Jersey
English Channel Islands
JE3 5BP
UK

Website: www.durrellwildlife.org
E-mail: info@durrellwildlife.org

'When asked, as I frequently am, why I should concern myself so deeply with the conservation of animal life, I reply that I have been very lucky and that throughout my life the world has given me the most enormous pleasure. But the world is as delicate and as complicated as a spider's web. If you touch one thread you send shudders running through all the other threads. We are not just touching the web we are tearing great holes in it.'

GERALD DURRELL, 1925–95

Throughout his career, Richard Johnstone-Scott has been instrumental in determining the moves of a number of animals into potential breeding situations. In 1993 he was appointed to act as joint-species coordinator for the Western Lowland Gorilla in the UK. Richard is an enthusiastic wildlife artist; he is married and has three children.

Jambo

A Gorilla's Story

RICHARD JOHNSTONE-SCOTT

Michael O'Mara Books Limited

First published in Great Britain in 1995 by
Michael O'Mara Books Limited
9 Lion Yard
Tremadoc Road
London SW4 7NQ

Michael O'Mara Books Limited paperback edition first
published in 2006

A CIP catalogue for this book is available from the British Library

ISBN (10 digit): 1-84317-234-8
ISBN (13 digit): 978-1-84317-234-5

1 3 5 7 9 10 8 6 4 2

www.mombooks.com

Designed and typeset in 12pt Garamond by Barrie Carr

Printed and bound in Great Britain by
Clays Ltd, St Ives plc

TO THE MEMORY OF MY PARENTS,
JOAN AND JOHNNIE

Gorilla – it seems as if he was born with a patent of nobility among Apes . . . in comparison to a chimpanzee holds his head higher producing the impression that he belongs to a better class of society

von Hermes, quoted by Brehm, 1896

CONTENTS

CONTENTS

ACKNOWLEDGMENTS

It had always been my intention, at some point in my keeping career, to attempt to write about the large number of gorillas and other marvellous creatures that I have had the extreme good fortune to work with over the years. Whether such an account would ever be suitable for publication was never a serious consideration for me, as really I visualized it being more of a personal reminder of the remarkable and fascinating individuality of each animal, and especially of those who came to have a quite profound effect upon my life.

So it was that when Trust Secretary, Simon Hicks, asked me if I would be prepared to put some text to a proposed book of photographs featuring Jambo and his family, I readily agreed. As I began researching Jambo's life, I very soon came to realize that a few humorous lines captioning a series of photographs, no matter how expertly taken, would never do him justice. There was simply too much to tell. Consequently, what was originally planned as a brief pictorial biography soon developed into an in-depth study of one of the most famous of all zoo gorillas. For me it became a far more demanding undertaking, yet one that I thoroughly enjoyed, and I have Simon to thank for creating the opportunity.

I am also extremely grateful to the Trust's veterinarian and general administrator, Tony Allchurch, for reading and improving the manuscript. Over the years, his veterinary skills and those of his former senior partner, Nick Blampied, have been invaluable in maintaining the general good health of the Jersey gorillas, and I therefore wish to add here my very sincere thanks to both for their services. My gratitude also extends to their colleagues in the human medical profession, who have always so generously given their time and expertise, thus ensuring that these superb animals receive the best possible care and attention.

I should also like to acknowledge the work of fellow keepers, both past and present, who have shared with me the responsibility of gorilla management and, in particular, those who cared for Jambo namely Phil Coffey, Jeremy Usher-Smith and Phil Arnold. A special word of recognition must go to another former staff member, Andy Wood, for his handling of the emergency situation, which arose when young Levan Merritt fell in to the gorilla enclosure.

In the course of the construction of this book I have endeavoured to provide information about gorillas in general. In particular, I very much appreciate the contributions made by Prof Dr Ernst M Lang, Don Cousins and the late David P Willoughby.

I am greatly indebted to Rachael Moore for the many hours of hard work that she has put in. A young lady of considerable patience and understanding, she uncomplainingly typed up page after page of my near illegible scribble, inserted much-needed punctuation, and corrected numerous spelling mistakes without laughing too loudly. She also assisted with some of the research, was solely responsible for drawing up Jambo's comprehensive genealogy chart, and remained cheerfully enthusiastic throughout.

My thanks also to the *Jersey Evening Post* for allowing me to include extracts from several articles and for granting me permission to reproduce a number of their splendid photographs. In particular, I would like to acknowledge the efforts of Jan Hadley, who so kindly searched through the photographic archives and then printed up my selection of pictures.

Next I would like to thank Phillip Coffey, the Trust's education officer, for kindly donating many of his excellent photographs and for his valuable comments on the manuscript.

I consider myself very fortunate to have entered zoo-keeping when I did and even more so to have worked for such reputable collections as the Jersey Wildlife Preservation Trust and Howletts Zoo Park, both highly acclaimed organizations founded by Gerald Durrell and John Aspinall respectively. To each of these remarkable men, I wish to express my deepest appreciation, firstly for their unique achievements in the fields of preservation and conservation, and secondly for enabling me to fulfil my ambition to work with exotic species, and later my desire to specialize in the care of anthropoids.

For their guidance and supervision during my initiation into ape-keeping, I shall always be grateful to the Trust's zoological director,

Jeremy Mallinson, and former curator of mammals, Stefan Ormrod. Without their help I might, in all ignorance, have returned to the more lucrative, yet far less rewarding occupation of bricklaying. Instead, I am pleased to add that since those early days, Jeremy, a most approachable director and one who shares my passion for gorillas, has continued to give me the benefit of his advice and support.

It is likely that the thrill of seeing gorillas in the wild would still be a long-awaited ambition of mine had it not been primarily for the pioneering fieldwork and dedication of the late Dian Fossey, a very special woman of courage and determination, whom I greatly admired. Though we corresponded, it is to my lasting regret that I was never able to pay her such a compliment in person. I should, however, like to thank two of her fellow research workers, Sandy Harcourt and Kelly Stewart, for so generously organizing time and accommodation for me up at Karisoke and for introducing me to the breath-taking sights of mountain gorillas in their natural habitat, incredible animals that once seen are never to be forgotten.

Anyone who has enjoyed a long and close association with wildlife will understand when I refer to there being emotional as well as physical demands in zoo-keeping. The responsibilities involved are often to be carried twenty-four hours a day, and this is especially the case when working with great apes. By their very nature these intriguing creatures automatically comprise a very large and significant part of a keeper's daily life. In effect, they become an extension of the family unit and sometimes they overshadow its human element. At Howletts, my relationship with a gorilla of extraordinary character prompted John Aspinall to write, in 1976, 'Richard Johnstone-Scott has a special attachment to Baby Doll and I would hazard a guess that she runs a close second to his wife in the race for his affections!' It was, in fact, true that Baby Doll or Yaounde, as she had originally been named, despite her tomboyish ways, and general unpredicability, had shared with me a trusting gorilla/keeper partnership for more than a decade. We just seemed to get along.

Being married to a zoo keeper, Jennifer had early on become

quite used to such competition. However, she has also experienced through me the moments of ecstacy and agony that only working with animals can bring, and for her unfailing support and encouragement, particularly through the difficult times, my eternal gratitude.

Finally, to Jambo and his family, and all those gorillas I have known, my respect and affectionate thanks for enriching my life by allowing me into theirs . . . and for only occasionally reminding me that I am merely human.

Richard A Johnstone-Scott
Jersey Wildlife Preservation Trust, 1994

PREFACE

Very few people, when confronted with the sight of a physically mature male gorilla, can refrain from expressing their feelings in some way. Either they will pass comment, be it complimentary or derogatory or, as in some cases, an unintelligible vocalization may be all that is managed, perhaps one not dissimilar to that emitted by the early adventurers when encountering his awe-inspiring presence for the first time.

The primeval features and incredible physique seem designed to intimidate, yet he remains capable through his actions and mannerisms of stimulating our curiosity to the point of haunting our imagination.

Having evolved simultaneously with man, the gorilla is descended from a primate ancestry of a line distinct from that which diverged to produce humans some five to ten million years ago, and is therefore a cousin greatly removed.

Stories that such a huge anthropoid existed were first recounted by Hanno, a Carthaginian admiral and explorer, who is believed to have come across wild hairy men and women during his historic voyage of discovery around the west coast of Africa, circa 500 BC. However, though it remains questionable whether his reports actually describe gorillas, chimpanzees or baboons, the name he gave to these man-like creatures, translated, was 'gorillai'. Not surprisingly, there are a number of additional theories as to how this word came into being, but regardless of whichever may appear to be the most feasible, there is no doubt that even today 'gorilla' remains a name that, for the less enlightened, still conjures up images of ferocious giant apes, with little or no suggestion of the placid and reserved animals that they really are.

When looking at its geographical distribution, it is perhaps understandable that more than one race of gorilla has been identified. Yet shortly after the turn of the century, it seemed a little extreme that systematists should have listed no fewer than fifteen different species and sub-species. Subsequently, confusion reigned until 1929, when a certain Harold J Coolodge provided sufficient taxonomic evidence to reduce the number to one species and two sub-species, namely:

1 The Western Lowland or Coastal Gorilla (*Gorilla gorilla gorilla*), as scientifically described by Dr Thomas S Savage and Dr Jeffries Wyman in 1874 and;

2 The Eastern or Mountain race (*Gorilla gorilla beringei*), named after the German colonial officer, Captain Oscar von Beringe, who was credited with its discovery in 1902. Living at high altitude, the Mountain Gorilla, which is known to frequent zones of up to 14,000 feet (4,700 metres), naturally possesses a thick, long and shaggy coat. While basically black in colour, the glossy sheen produces an almost bluish tinge to what is effectively an insulated and waterproof pelage.

The coat of the Western Lowland race is comparatively both shorter and lighter in colour and contains various shades of greys and browns, though the hair covering the shoulders and arms, especially of the adult males, is dark and similar in length to that of its mountain counterpart.

Today, due to detailed investigation of skull dimensions carried out in 1967 by Dr Colin Groves, three races of gorilla are now generally accepted by primatologists, the third being another Eastern form which had, in fact, already been recognized by some authorities many years before. They had named it *Gorilla gorilla graueri* after Rudolph Grauer, a German hunter, who had been responsible for 'collecting' (shooting) some sixteen specimens in 1908 and 1910.

Considered to be marginally larger than *Gorilla g. gorilla,* and *Gorilla g. beringei,* this Eastern Lowland race more closely resembles the latter, although its head is somewhat broader and face-shape longer and narrower in appearance. It is known to inhabit the dense lowland forests of the Mwenga-Fizi regions, Utu and Tshiaberimu in Eastern Zaire and the Bwindi Forest Reserve in Uganda, while the range of the Mountain Gorilla seems confined to the Virunga Volcanoes, west of Lake Kivu.

The domain of the Western Lowland Gorilla is more extensive and includes the tropical rain forests of southeast Nigeria, the Cameroons, Gabon, Equatorial Guinea, Cabinda, the Congo Brazzaville and the southern part of the Central African Republic.

Sadly, throughout much of their respective habitats, all three races are threatened with extermination. In many parts, there are no protected areas for them at all, and even in those remote places where their killing or capture is prohibited, such laws are poorly enforced.

Deforestation in the form of logging and mining and the encroachment of agriculture, which includes crop farming and cattle grazing, annually account for the disappearance of vast tracts of forest. In addition, the hunting of gorillas both for food and for the procurement of grisly trophies, such as their heads, hands and feet, which are then usually sold to European residents and tourists, also takes its ghastly toll of wild populations.

Statistics from field studies show the current status of these populations to be, in some areas, critical. For example, the number of Mountain Gorillas has been reduced to a few hundred individuals, although conservation measures initiated more than twenty years ago continue to maintain at least some control in the Rwandan section of the Virungas, the Parc National des Volcans.

With so few animals remaining, it is the opinion of many leading conservationists that, at this stage, to remove sufficient stock for captive breeding purposes would be counter-productive. Instead, they maintain that every effort should be made to maximize support for existing schemes such as the Fauna and Flora Preservation Society's Mountain Gorilla Project, and the Dian Fossey Gorilla Fund, which are committed to conserving the gorillas and many other remarkable creatures and the delicate ecosystem.

Meanwhile, despite inevitable habitat pressure, the two lowland sub-species are reported to be surviving in greater numbers. An estimated ten thousand or more of the Eastern race are thought to inhabit at least four well-protected areas in Zaire, while possibly up to ten times as many Western Lowland Gorillas, though clearly more vulnerable, occupy both primary and secondary forest totalling some 700,000 square kilometres (270,000 square miles). Census figures supplied by field workers Dr Caroline Tutin and Michael Fernandez suggest that almost 40 per cent of these animals are to be found in the Gabon alone.

Encouraging as these numbers may at first appear, when compared to the human populations of those same countries, they are very small indeed. More importantly, it should be emphasized that there is little effective protection for the gorilla throughout most of its West African range.

However, its survival in captivity seems virtually assured, as totals from a recent edition of the *International Studbook of the Gorilla*, compiled and edited by Dr Rosl Kirchshofer, suggest. At the end of 1991, there were 685 gorillas, 311 males and 374 females, living in 141 collections worldwide. Of these, 316 were wild-born and 369 bred in captivity. An 82.5 per cent survival rate of newborn infants was considered to be of particular significance, as, according to Dr Georgina Mace, a small-population geneticist working at the Institute of Zoology, Zoological Society of London, attaining an infant mortality rate of below 20 per cent would be a major factor in establishing a self-sustaining captive population.

PREFACE

As the situation with free-living gorillas deteriorates, so an increasing responsibility is placed upon reputable conservation-minded zoos to ensure that viable breeding groups are maintained. Meanwhile, a more direct approach to reintroduction is currently part of John Aspinall's gorilla orphanage project in the Congo. Established by the Howletts and Port Lympne Foundation and the government of the Republic of the Congo in 1989, its aim is to reintroduce orphaned and eventually captive-bred gorillas into the wild.

Here, young animals, all too often in appalling physical and emotional condition are brought in to receive medical treatment and extensive aftercare. Losses are inevitable, but, for those that survive, the second phase of their rescue is a carefully managed release programme carried out within the bounds of the new Lesio-Louna Gorilla Sanctuary. Relocating animals in this way, in their country of origin, signals a quite revolutionary approach to gorilla conservation, which itself has come a long way since its humble beginnings in the mid-1950s, when the first captive birth was recorded.

A little over twenty years ago, the Jersey Wildlife Preservation Trust proudly made its first of many contributions to the international gorilla breeding programme, following the arrival of a young black-backed male, who in his lifetime was to become known throughout the world as perhaps the perfect ambassador for his species.

His name was Jambo.

IN THE BEGINNING

It was a little over fourteen years ago that I returned to work at the Jersey Zoo for the third time. Had it not been for an outbreak of yellow jaundice among the staff some fourteen years earlier, I might never have started there at all.

I had, in my search to earn a living working with animals, managed to add my name to London Zoo's extensive waiting list, but that was about all. Other collections had not even bothered to respond to my numerous applications for a keeping position and, bitterly disappointed, I was contemplating trying my luck abroad. As a young man, my father had travelled to New Zealand and then Australia, but, while some of his many occupations had a certain adventurous appeal – stockman on a sheep farm and gold prospector in the Blue Mountains – all I really wanted was to get a job in a zoo or a wildlife sanctuary.

Then suddenly, due to illness, there was a desperate shortage of staff in the Channel Island Zoo and I eagerly took my chance. Having long been an avid reader of his books, I had written about a dozen times in all to Gerald Durrell, begging for employment. Each of my letters pleaded with him to release me from the drudgery of bricklaying. Eventually my persistence paid off and quite unexpectedly on 25 June 1965 I got my long-awaited break into zoo-keeping. 'I shall willingly take on any job,' I had rashly stated, and for the majority of my trial period, 'any job' was exactly what I was expected to do.

Having stepped from the comfort of a London-to-Jersey flight, it was a bit of a shock an hour later to find myself staggering about knee-deep in cage cleanings and overripe offal from the slaughterhouse, while assisting with the unenviable procedure of loading 'Paddy's' wagon with zoo refuse, destined for the local dump. This not particularly pleasant twice-weekly duty had the more wily keepers slinking off to perform 'vitally important' tasks elsewhere, usually at the furthest point from where this ancient vehicle was parked. Consequently Paddy, the owner-driver, and I soon got to know one another rather well.

Shovelling lorry loads of fresh woodshavings and sawdust into the storage sheds was another equally rewarding experience, especially on hot sunny days when the shavings would stick to a perspiring body like glue, and sawdust clogged every orifice. Creosoting fences and painting bars on cage fronts were a definite improvement, yet neither of these seemingly endless undertakings provided quite the same degree of satisfaction as did removing by hand the stodge of fish entrails and other delights from the otter-pool drain. That was, as I remember, my first direct animal-keeping duty, and one that produced a heady aroma, guaranteed to penetrate the most severely blocked of sinuses.

From an early age I had always been allowed to keep various forms of animal life, and had progressed to caring for more exotic creatures shortly before leaving school. A Senegal bushbaby (*Galago senegalensis*) and an Indian grey mongoose (*Herpestes edwardsi*) named Igm (Igam) had been the pride of my menagerie, which was to be tragically consumed by a fire only months before my departure to Jersey. Though he was not especially tame, I would often take Igm with me to work which, in retrospect, was rather an irresponsible thing to do, as on one unforgettable day he severely nipped Old Jack, my long-suffering general foreman. This unfortunate incident occurred during an 'instruction to apprentices on how to read site plans' session, a thoroughly boring hour, compulsory for all young, potential tradesmen.

On this particular afternoon, with my usual lack of enthusiasm, I had shuffled reluctantly into the office, taken Igm out of my jacket and placed him, as I had done several times before, on a toolbox situated at the top of a large sloping desk, on which there were also spread a number of building construction drawings. Almost immediately, the clerk of works, who was never entirely happy with the presence of such an unpredictable pet, let out shrill exclamations of alarm and dismay, as Igm promptly urinated over the plans. Both clerk and foreman then panicked and tried to salvage what they could, but in their excitement failed to take into account the nervous disposition and lightening reflexes of *Herpestes edwardsi*. Poor 'Old Jack', he received an extremely painful bite to his right hand, the intensity of which I was only too familiar with and so was fully able to appreciate his need to expel such an outpouring of loud and colourful language. The result of this was an early finish for both me and my mongoose. So, stuffing a highly odorous Igm back into my jacket, I left hurriedly with Jack's fond farewells ringing in my ear: 'Go 'ome ya little bl. . . . r and take that rat wiv ya, bl . . . y dangerous fing!'

However, within a few weeks of my arriving at the zoo, all thoughts of bricklaying and building sites quickly faded into obscurity as now, instead of being subjected daily to the deafeningly penetrating noises produced by compressors, cement mixers and pneumatic drills, I was able to enjoy the echoing calls of crested seriemas (*Cariama cristata*), which are large strutting birds from South America, West African colobus monkeys (*Colobus polykomos*) and ring-tailed lemurs (*Lemur catta*) from Madagascar. It was exactly the kind of tranquil setting that I had read about in Gerald Durrell's book, *Menagerie Manor*.

Working and living at Les Augrès Manor in those early days was a marvellous experience. The collection was still in its infancy and it was a time of breaking new ground in the management and breeding of many rare and endangered species. It was also a time of learning for everyone concerned, which created a special kind of camaraderie among the predominantly young and enthusiastic team.

Having finally been accepted as a permanent member of staff, I was, to my great delight and satisfaction, assigned to the mammal section, which was divided into two departments. 'Outside Mammals' included the big cats, bears, tapirs, peccaries, badgers, otters, dingoes (which frequently went walkabout!), civets and baboons; the Mammal House contained an enormous variety of small mammals, among which were various species of monkey, as well as some of the lesser primates, lemurs, marmosets, tamarins and, at the bottom of the scale, tupias or tree shrews. There were also several kinds of mongoose, the largest being the impressive giant marsh species, *Atilax paludinosus,* and a host of armadillos. Add to this, long-nosed echidna (*Tachyglossus aculeatus*), fennec fox (*Fennecus zerda*), giant malabar squirrel (*Ratuta indica maxima*) and the mysterious binturong (*Arctictis binturong*), and it will present a fair picture of just how diverse the collection was. Then, of course, there were the apes: a mixture of chimpanzees (*Pan troglodytes troglodytes*), Bornean orang-utans (*Pongo pygmaeus pygmaeus*) and, for me the most alluring of all, the gorillas, namely N'pongo and Nandi who, to my surprise, I discovered were both female.

Just why I was so attracted to them I am not entirely sure, because, if anything, I found them rather intimidating. Compared to their high-spirited neighbours, the chimpanzees Cholmondley, Sheena and Bibi, and the more placid, yet equally outgoing nature of the young orang-utans, Oscar and Bali, both N'pongo and Nandi seemed very aloof and quite private individuals. Nevertheless, I was intrigued and instinctively felt that the apes were for me, though I very soon realized that it was not going to be quite as simple as that.

Anthropoids, as well as being highly intelligent, are also creatures of great sensitivity, who require time to adapt to new situations. Changes of keeper, in particular, can be fraught with problems which, in some cases, may be prolonged either because man distrusts ape or ape distrusts or even dislikes man. Taking over animals who have enjoyed a lengthy cohesive relationship with one or two favoured keepers or those who may have had to endure the varying attitudes of many, is rarely easy. For the new keeper, regardless of experience, there is no guarantee of acceptance.

During a probationary period of some four to six weeks, trainee keepers, while learning the basic cleaning and feeding routines, would be encouraged to familiarize themselves with the apes. Then, provided that the outcome proved satisfactory, they would be expected to continue to work at forming a more trusting, 'through the bars', relationship. Any further development, which with certain individuals could result in regular hands-on contact, would then be decided largely by the nature of the animals concerned, and the ability of the keeper to plumb the depths of the anthropoid mind.

Looking back, I must have been making a fairly good impression as my first real insight into the captive world of the gorilla, 'from the other side of the bars', came quite unexpectedly. It was an experience that to this day I can picture in quite vivid detail, despite it having taken place all those years ago.

It was not until we were securely locked within the claustrophobic and dimly lit confines of the safety area that I began to reconsider my somewhat impulsive decision to accompany Stefan into the cage to assist with the feeding. As curator of mammals, Stefan Ormrod had mastered the technique of wording suggestions to sound like orders, which I, in my position as trainee keeper, invariably obeyed. Under his supervision, I had eagerly carried out my initial two months' duties, and had subsequently come both to trust and respect his judgment, but his latest proposal suddenly had me doubting his sanity. 'I think it's about time you got to know them a little better. Why not help me out later this morning?' 'Sure Steff, if you think it's all right.' My unguarded reply was due to the fact that, at that precise moment, I was preoccupied with a rather irate mona monkey (*Cercopithecus mona*). Smiling at my dilemma, Stefan continued, 'Well, it's not as if you're a complete stranger to them, and to be honest, the longer you leave it, the more difficult it will be.' The mona gaped a threat and shook the branches. 'After coffee break then, once the feeds have been prepared.' 'Right-o Steff,' I gasped, and finally jammed the mona's perch into position. The monkey, unable to contain his excitement, urinated copiously and I made a damp exit.

Up until that morning my dealings with N'pongo and Nandi had been restricted to cage cleaning and, under my curator's watchful eye, feeding them through the bars. It was during one of these tentative feeding sessions that, even before the ever-alert Stefan could intervene, N'pongo had unceremoniously removed a sleeve from my shirt. Days later, a pocket from my one and only pair of jeans disappeared in similar fashion. Still, I had Stefan's assurance that such mischievous behaviour was, after all, of a solely playful nature. Had it been otherwise, then it could have been parts of my anatomy that had vanished through the bars!

A hum of gorilla sound now drowned Stefan's final instructions. Clutching a feed tray in each hand, I kept my eyes on his as he stooped to release the one bolt which now held the 9-centimetre (3 inch) thick metal-plated door closed. His lips continued to form words, though it was only a momentary lull in the deep resonant grumblings that enabled me to hear . . . to be inquisitive, but just stay close to me and . . . The grumblings of anticipation, now punctuated with cough grunts of frustration, engulfed his voice. The gorillas were hungry and becoming increasingly impatient.

As the bolt was drawn back, the vocalizations rose to highly pitched, excited whines. Shiny black fingers appeared around the edge of the door, and the musky, slightly sweet, smell of the inmates, an odour that I was soon to become all too familiar with, drifted into the safety porch.

'Hello 'pongo old girl.' Again a brief lull. 'Come on, Richard,' and Stefan, in a semi-crouched posture, pushed the door fully open and disappeared into the den. Casting a glance to the heavens and taking a deep breath, I bent to follow, but in my haste to keep up, I completely misjudged the waist-high opening, struck my forehead against the metal frame and slumped heavily to my knees before an extremely surprised, and clearly agitated, N'pongo. My hands, which instinctively clasped at what was left of my skull, automatically released the trays, showering a colourful assortment of fruits and vegetables on to the sawdust-covered floor. The next few seconds can best be described simply as chaotic, with the clanging of metal dishes, the guttural barkings of alarmed gorillas and the blasphemous cursings of a highly distraught curator serving to attract the attentions of a group of mid-morning visitors.

In the ensuing confusion, Stefan was whirled around and practically knocked off his feet, as both females, prompted into an immediate retreat by my startling entrance, took to their heels. Desperate to make amends, and doing my best to ignore the excruciating pain in my head, I snatched at the nearest items of food, while my red-faced superior, miraculously still armed with his bottles of diluted milk, fought to restore some semblance of order. Nandi, the smaller and less confident female, scurried to her usual feeding place – the shelf by the window – and was soon nervously accepting a drink. She gulped quickly, dribbling milk from her generously pinked lower lip, a feature which made her look as if she wore a permanent smile. The whites of her eyes flashed as she glanced anxiously from Stefan to me and then to N'pongo, as if seeking some reassurance from the latter.

'Come on, calm down. There, have a drink, good girl,' Stefan soothed through gritted teeth. 'Come here 'pongo, here's yours.' But N'pongo was in no mood for comforting. Quick to recover her composure and with hair bristling, she glared at me from the far side of the den. Her challenging barks halted my attempts to collect up the scattered food. I hesitated, momentarily intrigued by the vivid pink of her open mouth, which housed a perfect and formidable array of teeth. Immediately alert to the potential seriousness of the situation,

Stefan, to his great credit, remained calm and repeated his offer of drinks, using that authoritative tone of his to masterful effect. 'No, 'pongo, that's enough, come on, have a drink, 'pongo drink! Then, sidling slowly away from Nandi, he reached out towards her companion, proffering the milk.

To my immense relief, N'pongo's threats gradually subsided into a series of rapid grunts as she grasped the neck of the bottle and sucked greedily, but her hostile eyes never left me. I was absolutely terrified, and shook visibly. I looked to Stefan and waited for the order to leave, but it didn't come, and N'pongo's grunts melted into grumbles of pleasure.

'Now, collect Nandi's share of the fruit, put it in her dish, don't drop it, and hand them to her carefully, a piece at a time.' His instructions were delivered clearly and concisely, but Stefan made no effort to conceal the exasperation in his voice. With his free hand, he raked his fingers through his closely cropped curly hair, wiped his glistening brow on his forearm and added, 'Talk to her, apologize for being such an idiot and, with a bit of luck, we might both leave here intact!'

Grateful for the chance to redeem myself, I gathered up Nandi's feed and eased my way across the cage to her. The audience on the opposite side of the glass, having increased in number now, jostled for a better view. So far, it had all been highly entertaining.

Nandi tensed at my approach, but soon held out an open leathery palm to receive a bruised orange. Clutching it in powerful fingers, she first raised it to her flattened nose then, having decided it was edible, began neatly removing the peel with her teeth, gurgling as she did so. 'Good girl,' I mumbled as the orange vanished in two juicy mouthfuls and, now slightly more relaxed, Nandi gestured for a second. This was quickly followed up by two apples, a carrot, a pear and finally, the much-favoured banana, of which, interestingly, the skin was consumed first. Her gurgles of contentment continued for as long as the food lasted, and my steady flow of compliments also seemed to be appreciated. At last I was making progress and suddenly I noticed that I was no longer trembling.

Stefan was enjoying similar success with N'pongo, but as she squatted on her feeding platform situated in the centre of the den, it was obvious that she still viewed me with a great deal of suspicion. 'Here you are 'pongo, try an apple. Mmm . . . that's good, isn't it? N'pongo grumbled and chewed loudly, her incredibly strong jaw muscles flexing visibly from lower cheek to cranium. Though only eight years of age, she simply oozed confidence, and the disdainful looks she cast in my direction made me feel very humble indeed.

Both gorillas had been wild-caught, taken as infants from their forest homes in West Africa. Having miraculously survived the trauma of capture and transportation at the merciless hands of hunters and animal dealers, they now, at least, had found a sanctuary, albeit in captivity. Some were of the opinion that Nandi's horrific experiences had left her scarred both mentally and physically, her nervous disposition being attributed to the severe ill-treatment she had undoubtedly received, a theory supported by the presence of a now barely visible machete wound across the top of her head.

Watching her now, busily engaged in removing the white inner pith from some remaining scraps of orange peel, apparently oblivious to the staring eyes of the public, I suddenly felt a deep sympathy for the squat little female. Though dominant, N'pongo was her closest ally, without whose company she might never have adapted to life in a captive environment. However, being subordinate, the onus was constantly on Nandi to watch for any signs from her companion that might indicate a possible change of mood or intention, especially as N'pongo was not averse to occasionally helping herself to Nandi's food. In order to minimize her losses, the latter had to remain alert and be ready to take action. Either she would surrender a single food item and then move off carrying the rest, or she would simply take refuge behind her keeper.

Nandi, still nibbling orange peel, glanced continuously over my shoulder. Following her example, I half-turned to look at N'pongo, and was immediately reprimanded by my sharp-eyed superior. 'If you stare at her like that, she will never settle,' snapped Stefan. 'Pay attention to Nandi, and give 'pongo a chance to calm down.' The strict but sound advice was endorsed by a prolonged belch vocalization from N'pongo, as she chomped her way through a pear. So, murmuring something derogatory about curators, I turned back to Nandi. It seemed that we, in our respective lowly positions, shared at least one thing in common . . . perhaps she sensed that as well.

Suddenly, without warning, N'pongo's grumbles of pleasure ceased, and Nandi, like a sprinter on starting blocks, rose instantly to all fours, her eyes locked on her companion. N'pongo's feed dish crashed to the ground and cough grunts of renewed agitation echoed across the cage. Lowering her bulk to the floor, she then poised herself for a charge in my direction. Immediately behind me, Nandi answered the vocalized threats and, despite my predicament, I found myself questioning why she should be getting involved. Whatever her reasons, Nandi's response briefly checked N'pongo's move, which in turn gave Stefan the chance to act. Voicing yet another blasphemous statement, he boldly confronted the bad-tempered female. 'That's enough 'pongo. Come on. Pack it up, you silly . . . I said that's enou . . .' Having pushed Stefan aside, she seized my left leg in a vice-like grip and galloped off towards the slide opening, which led to the outside area.

Once again, I found myself in the sawdust, only this time I was being dragged through it at a rate of knots. As luck would have it, on reaching the opening, my outstretched, flailing arms and legs prevented me from following N'pongo through and instead I came to an abrupt and painful halt against the doorframe. The next thing I remember is feeling Nandi's weight on my chest, as she trundled over me to join N'pongo outside. 'Come on, that's enough for now,' Stefan panted and he pulled me roughly to my feet. 'They obviously like you, but let's go before they get too friendly.' So, much to the disappointment of the audience, we finally made our exit. 'Do you play with them like that every day?' asked someone as we pushed our way through the gathering outside. I tried to respond, but found myself too numb to reply.

It was several months and many eventful encounters later before N'pongo began to show signs of accepting me. I clearly remember the smug feeling of accomplishment when I received my first real friendly reception from her.

In contrast, Nandi and I always seemed to get on, although there was very little physical contact between us, as she rarely allowed herself to be stroked, which may have stemmed from her unpleasant experiences as an infant. Nevertheless, occasionally she would playfully ambush me as I entered the enclosure, which usually meant that I had to return to the kitchen to refill the milk bottles. Still, it made her feel good, as her triumphant chest beats indicated.

Although Stefan enjoyed an enviable rapport with the gorillas, their greatest affections, and particularly those of N'pongo, were reserved for Jeremy – that is, Jeremy Mallinson, Jersey Zoo's first gorilla keeper and now the zoological director of the JWPT. His almost regimental, no-nonsense attitude, clearly a trait of his Rhodesian army days, combined with an excellent understanding of the two totally different characters, enabled him to maintain a close, trusting relationship with even the temperamental and mischievous N'pongo. Working alongside Jeremy was an education in itself. Watching and listening to him discuss topics ranging from current affairs to the state of the weather with the grumbling females at feeding times, though amusing, was also a lesson in communication. 'It's not so much what you say, dear boy, but the tone of voice that counts.' Of course, it's common sense when you think about it.

There was, however, one occasion when no matter what tone of voice was used, N'pongo was not prepared to listen. Though before continuing, I should perhaps point out that clearly another past connection with his military service is Jeremy's impeccable appearance: he is rarely seen without a collar and tie, even when servicing cages or feeding animals.

On one particular summer's day, in shirt and tie, he accompanied me in to the gorilla enclosure to share the afternoon feeding, which went well until N'pongo began to admire Jeremy's rather regimental-looking tie. 'Yes, dear girl, isn't that interesting, you like that, do you?' N'pongo grumbled and began to pull, gently at first, and then . . . ''pongo, this is a very expensive tie, and not for playing with.' More enthusiastic grumbles from N'pongo, who then decided to descend from the waist-high platform to the floor, with the tie still clenched firmly in her powerful fist. 'Now, come along, 'pongo. What do you think you're doing? I am not impressed, dear girl.' Jeremy was now bent forward and being led slowly towards the slide opening to the outside area. 'Excuse me, Richard, dear man. I think I may need some assistance,' and, still in tow, he disappeared, muttering through the doorway.

Leaving Nandi to finish off her food, I followed with the intention of trying to distract N'pongo with a few peanuts. However, by now the tie had become uncomfortably tight around Jeremy's neck, and he rightly decided that more direct action was necessary. 'I think you ought to go back to the kitchen and bring me a knife. It doesn't look as if she's going to let go and . . .' he croaked. A knife! At first I thought that was a bit drastic. However, on my return, I was simply instructed to cut the offending tie inches below the now minute knot. 'Thank you, dear boy,' gasped Jeremy, and then to the still grumbling N'pongo, 'Well, what have you got to say for yourself? I shall be sending you the bill!' Even more amusing was the fact that Jeremy, possibly forgetting that his tie had been somewhat reduced in size, continued to sport the remainder of it throughout the rest of the day!

So it was that I eased myself into the role of ape-keeper, and subsequently embarked on a career which, in its first four years, was to take me temporarily to the London Zoo for a summer season, back to Jersey and then, in 1969, to the private animal sanctuary at Howletts in southeast Kent.

Working for its founder and owner, John Aspinall, proved to be both a challenging and exciting experience. It was a time when the true potential of his zoo was just beginning to emerge, especially that of the gorilla collection. Already one of the finest, it rapidly became transformed into the nucleus of what has since become the world's largest single captive population.

During my ten years at Howletts, the number of gorillas increased from six to twenty-six, which comprised at least three main groupings, plus several other permutations. I was in my element and, though entirely my own choice, leaving them was incredibly difficult, and I found myself requiring a very lengthy period of adjustment. After all, it is impossible to work closely with such demanding animals without becoming emotionally involved, as once you get to know them, they simply take over your life.

However, having been attracted by the prospect of creating a new group at Jersey, I returned once more to the Trust, to take up duties as section head of apes. It was August 1979 and, though I was back on fairly familiar ground and able to renew old acquaintances with the likes of N'pongo and Nandi, it was also my first opportunity to introduce myself to the imposing figure of Jambo.

This particularly handsome male was then approximately eighteen years of age, and although he was supremely confident, with his jet black arms and swaggering gait, he was also surprisingly approachable. I soon felt comfortable in his presence and liked him immensely and sincerely hoped that, in time, he would come to feel the same way about me.

A Family Tree showing Jambo's relationships and progeny

ACHILLA
B. in wild
1947
Died 1986

STEPHI
Born in wild
1949
Died 1981

JAMBO
B. Basle Zoo 17 April 1961
Arrived Jersey 1972,
Died 16 September 1992

1 NANDI
B. in wild 1959
Arrived Jersey 1961
Died 3 April 1992

2 N'PONGO
B. in wild 1957
Arrived Jersey 1959

3 KISHKA
B. Howletts Zoo 1978
Arrived Jersey 1984

4 G-ANN
B. Oklahoma,
USA 1979
Arrived Jersey
1983

5 JULIA
B. in wild 1981
Arrived Jersey from the
Gambia 1990

ASSUMBO
B. Jersey 1973
Sent Tuycross 1976

ZAIRE
B. Jersey 1974
Sent London 1984

MAMFE
B. Jersey 1973
Sent Tuycross, UK 1976

TATU
B. Jersey 1975
Sent Oklahoma, USA 1983

SAKINA
B. Jersey 1986

BAMENDA
B. Jersey 1976
Sent to Howletts 1984

KAKINGA
B. Jersey 1978
Sent Calgary Canada 1984

KUMBA
B. Jersey 1976
Sent London 1979
Now at Chessington

N'GOLA
B. Jersey 1977
Sent Zurich Zoo 1984

MOTABA
B. Jersey 1983
Sent Melbourne,
Australia 1990

KUMI
B. Jersey 1981
Died 1981

RAFIKI
B. Jersey 1984
Sent St Louis, USA 1991

HLALA KAHILLI
B. Jersey 1988

ASATO
B. Jersey 1991

LEVAN MERRITT

'Where's the really big gorilla? You know, the one that saved the little boy?' 'It was amazing, he was so gentle. Do you think he understood?' 'He was simply wonderful. What was his name? Jambo? Yes! That's it, Jambo . . . So where is he, where's Jambo?' Requests and comments such as these, as well as countless others relating to an eventful August afternoon in 1986, are still frequently made by visitors to the gorilla complex at the Jersey Wildlife Preservation Trust.

It seems that everyone remembers Jambo! The zoo's magnificent sil-verback had greatly enhanced an already marked popularity by his exemplary behaviour towards young Levan Merritt, following the unfortunate child's fall into the gorilla enclosure on that busy Sunday afternoon. An incredulous public witnessed the incident, while an equally astounded worldwide TV audience later watched the dramatic video pictures taken by a zoo visitor. Hundreds of thousands of people, many of whom took time to contact the Trust to praise the gentleness and sensitivity of the gorillas, were clearly moved by what they had seen.

The sight of Jambo's massive frame reaching out and tenderly stroking Levan with huge padded hands, then sniffing inquisitively before towering protectively over the dwarfed form of the stricken boy drew enormous response from both the public and the media. Jambo hit the international headlines.

Addressed simply to Jambo, letters and cards of admiration and congratulation flooded in from all over the world. There were dona-tions too. Children sent their pocket money, senior citizens sent what they could, even the US Army felt the need to contribute. Boxes of bananas arrived along with other gifts, plus numerous requests for autographed photographs of the anthropoid hero.

Then there were other forms of tribute, such as this composition from 'Four Hard-Working Mums' at Electrolux, Luton:

> A little boy you did save
> From terror and danger, you're so brave!
> The other gorillas you kept at bay
> So the four of us would like to say
> Thank you Jambo! Hip! Hip! Hooray!

Meanwhile, a Mr C A Taylor, having been inspired to capture a scene from the incident on canvas, generously presented his work to the Trust. One postcard to Jambo, supposedly sent from his sister Quarta at Basle Zoo in Switzerland, conveyed love and praises from his mother Achilla, his son Tam Tam and various nieces and nephews.

On the whole, the press reported events fairly accurately. Even they seemed to have difficulty in sensationalizing something which had, in reality, been quite sensational. The cartoonists, though, thoroughly enjoyed themselves. One quoted Jambo as saying, 'It's humiliating to think that humans are descended from us . . .' A masterpiece by Mac of the *Daily Mail*, depicting Jambo as part of the Prime Minister's cabinet reshuffle, was later presented to the Trust by the artist and Channel Television. So, because Jambo and his family had simply been themselves, a potentially disastrous situation became a story which enraptured the world. The initial response of the gorillas to the sudden appearance of the child and the ensuing human commotion had been to do no more than investigate the stranger in their midst. Understandably, Jambo had led the way, whilst in the wake of his majestic stride trotted Nandi, small in stature for an adult female, but strong enough in character to enjoy both a senior position in the hierarchy and the closest of relationships with the silverback. Somewhat hampered by her two-and-a-half-year-old son Motaba, who rode jockey-fashion on her back, she laboured to keep up as the other group members closed in at a more leisurely pace.

'Now, you all know how keen I am to achieve a compassionate, caring and gentle image . . .'

Then, amidst a chorus of anguished cries from the crowded walls, some twelve feet above, Jambo carefully descended the grassy slope and approached the small unconscious figure, which lay motionless and bleeding in the rainwater gully on the north side of the enclosure. He stopped on the concrete surround and leaned down and forwards, not the most comfortable of positions for such a large animal, and sniffed the little stranger several times. Far from satisfied, he then stepped directly over him and tested other parts of his body with additional explorative sniffs.

Meanwhile, Nandi and offspring, having been joined by Rafiki, a younger half-brother to Motaba, arrived together on the scene and, following their patriarch's example, began sniffing cautiously, while at the same time edging gradually closer and closer. Then, with the adventurous Rafiki crouched within arm's-reach of the still human form, the ever-watchful Jambo decided to intervene and deliberately placed himself between the boy and his inquisitive family. It was a gesture clearly understood by all of them – Do not touch! It was also the action that was later interpreted as protecting the child. However, though he appeared to exhibit a degree of natural concern, it is more likely that Jambo was simply satisfying his own curiosity before allowing the others an opportunity to investigate, or perhaps keeping them away until he was sure that no danger existed. For whatever reason, Jambo, after further sniffing, settled back on his powerful haunches and stared up with dark appraising eyes at the mass of expectant faces. He knew where the child had come from, but why?

He studied the human expressions for practically a full minute and almost seemed to be listening to the comments of the fearful audience: 'Oh my God! Get away, you brute!' Then, calmly, he lowered his huge head and resumed his interest in the helpless child. The crowd stirred uneasily, and then gasped in unison as Jambo reached down and carefully lifted part of the boy's clothing. Intrigued by what lay beneath, he gently brushed a dark leathery finger against the exposed pale skin. Then, in typical gorilla fashion, he raised his fingers to his broad flat nose and smelled them, testing once again for scent . . . Homo sapiens.

Shortly afterwards, little Levan, roused by the pain of his injuries, began to regain consciousness. His pitiful cries, which rapidly increased in both frequency and volume, startled gorillas and humans alike and, in almost immediate response, members of the crowd began frantically to issue a variety of desperate warnings: 'Don't move Son! Keep quiet and lie still! Such well-meant instructions only added to the confusion and panic, further upsetting Levan's already highly distraught parents, who were caught up in the surge of spectators.

Below them Jambo, who had coolly controlled the situation from a strategic position barely a few paces from the little boy, now suddenly became visibly disturbed. Rising to all fours, he paused, staring down at the child's clumsy, uncoordinated movements. Then, at the onset of a fresh outburst of screams, he left, making a hasty, but fairly dignified, retreat towards the gorilla house. The hydraulic doors hissed noisily open to admit him; his 'burbling' females followed anxiously, while the ever inquisitive Rafiki, having lingered for as long as he dared, scampered madly after them.

The timely departure of Jambo and his family, however, was not to be the last act of the drama. As the door closed behind the silverback, Hobbit, an unrelated seven-year-old male, who had until that moment been confined to the inside quarters, barged his way out through the cluster of startled females queuing to enter.

His unexpected appearance was met with renewed gasps of horror from the crowds and, clearly excited by the commotion, the young male stomped impressively towards the subject of their concern. The situation demanded quick decisions from Andy Wood who, in my absence, was acting as section head: Hobbit's boisterous ways and mischievous nature posed perhaps an even greater threat than the rest of the group put together. Consequently, Andy took it upon himself boldly to enter the outside enclosure and assume what had been Jambo's approximate position, next to the now conscious and highly distressed little Levan. Within minutes he had been gallantly joined by Gary Clark of the bird staff, who unhesitatingly dropped down over the enclosure wall to offer what assistance he could. Together, the two men faced up to a series of galloping approaches from Jersey's second-ranking male gorilla. Meanwhile, ambulanceman Brian Fox, having clambered down behind Gary, quickly assessed the child's injuries before calling for a rope to be lowered. Promptly securing it about himself, he cradled his tearful patient safely in his arms and signalled to be hauled up and out of the compound, to spontaneous and rapturous applause from the public. Andy and Gary also made safe exits, leaving a rather frustrated Hobbit to his displays. The courage shown by both keepers and Brian Fox would later be deservedly acknowledged with bravery awards. But the individual whom most people were quick to credit with young Levan's survival was at that moment to be found inside, quietly enjoying a bonus feed of fruit and vegetables.

A STEP AWAY FROM KING KONG

Once Levan Merritt had made a rapid and complete recovery from his injuries, he was soon able to accompany his parents on a return visit to the zoo, a trip organized by the *Sunday Mirror* newspaper. Levan's reunion with Jambo – this time separated by windows of toughened glass – was widely covered by the press. Despite the explosions from a battery of flash bulbs, Jambo remained quite impassive as young Levan posed happily alongside him, saying, 'He looked after me, didn't he?' and, 'Jambo is my friend and I want to be a keeper when I grow up!'

The naturally relaxed and inoffensive behaviour exhibited by Jambo and his family throughout the original incident helped to confirm the arguments of experts who have long maintained that gorillas are not the monsters of popular myth. In the words of television zoologist, Sir David Attenborough: 'Human beings grow up with the notion of beauty and the beast and that was the theme successfully traded on by films like *King Kong* . . . Sadly, logic shows us that the exact opposite actually applies. It is human beings who are the aggressive primates.'

The Fauna and Flora Preservation Society (FFPS) used Jambo's gesture to try to dispel the traditional image of the gorilla as a combination of King Kong, the abominable snowman and monster of the swamps. The society's executive secretary, John Burton, claimed that much of the gorilla's evil reputation stemmed from the desire of generations of big-game hunters to convince admirers at home that they had shot a ruthless adversary, and not a frightened animal that simply wanted to be left in peace.

One of the earliest such culprits has to be the 'intrepid' American-born explorer, Paul Belloni Du Chaillu, considered to be the first white man to face a living adult gorilla in its natural habitat. In 1861 Du Chaillu published a sensationalized account of his experiences:

Suddenly, as we were yet creeping along in a silence which made even a heavy breath seem loud and distinct, the woods were at once filled with a tremendous barking roar; then underbush swayed rapidly just ahead, and presently stood before us, an immense gorilla. He had gone through the jungle on all fours but, when he saw our party, he erected himself and looked us boldly in the face. He stood about a dozen yards from us, and was a sight I think I shall never forget. Nearly six feet high, with immense body, huge chest and great muscular arms, with fiercely-glaring large, deep grey eyes, and a hellish expression of face, which seemed to me some nightmare vision – there stood not afraid of us; he stood there and beat his breast with his large fists till it resounded like an immense bass drum (which is his mode of bidding defiance), meantime giving vent to roar after roar.

The roar of the gorilla is the most singular and awful noise heard in these African woods. It begins with a sharp bark, like an angry dog, then glides into a deep bass roll, which literally and closely resembles the roll of distant thunder along the sky, for which I have sometimes been tempted to take it where I did not see the animal. . .

His eyes began to flash fiercer fire as we stood motionless on the defensive, and the crest of short hair, which stands on his forehead began to twitch rapidly up and down, while his powerful fangs were shown as he sent forth a thunderous roar, and now truly he reminded me of nothing but some hellish dream-

Paul Du Chaillu shoots his first gorilla. From Paul Du Chaillu, *Explorations in Equatorial Africa*

creature – a being of that hideous order, half-man, half-beast, which we find pictured by old artists in some representations of the infernal regions. He advanced a few steps, then stopped to utter that hideous roar again, advanced again, and finally stopped when at a distance of about six yards from us. And here, as he began another of his roars and beating his breast in rage, we fired and killed him.

In total contrast to such highly sensationalized accounts, the modern-day works of Dr George J Schaller and the even more recent publications of the late Dr Dian Fossey have presented a scientific and enchanting view of the private life of one of man's closest living relatives. Their extensive studies in the field have shown the gorilla to be a shy, retiring vegetarian, who occasionally eats grubs for protein and lives for the most part in compatible family groups.

JAMBO

Long before receiving public acclaim as the gorilla who saved the little boy, Jambo was already very well known in zoo circles. His birth and all-important rearing by his mother, Achilla, are recognized as events of great significance in the management and breeding of gorillas.

On 17 April 1961, at the world-famous Basle Zoologischer Garten in Switzerland, Jambo became the first male gorilla to be born in captivity; he would also be the first captive-born gorilla to be successfully reared by his mother. Both of the females previously born in captivity – Colo, born in Columbus Zoo, Ohio, USA in 1956, and Goma, born to Achilla herself in Basle in 1959 – had had to be removed from their mothers for hand-rearing. Nineteen months after Goma's arrival, Achilla made amends when Jambo was born, and a piece of zoo history went into the record books.

Jambo's name – most people, including myself, actually called him Yambo – comes from a Swahili word of greeting, meaning 'Hello' or 'How do you do?' It was given to him by Professor Ernst

H Lang, then director of Basle Zoo, who with his wife had been responsible for the hand-rearing of Goma. Lang recorded the climax of Achilla's 252-day gestation:

> This was the first time that a gorilla birth had been at least partly observed. An assistant keeper entering Achilla's cage at 7.00 am noted her sitting, as usual, in the automobile tyre that served as both toy and nest. Half an hour later, he came back. Rising, Achilla, greeting him with a grunt, placed her hand beneath her body, and held out an infant in her hand.
>
> She curled up with it in the tyre. At first, the tiny newcomer lay in her arm, turned away from her breast, just as Goma had done nineteen months before. But during the day the picture changed. Achilla appeared more relaxed and moved her infant from one position to another.
>
> The young gorilla was completely helpless, in the same state as a human baby at birth. He weighed only about four pounds. His ability to grip was scarcely developed, as compared to that of chimpanzees and orang-utans, which cling tightly to the mother's fur from the moment of birth. For the most part, the baby stretched out his arms with hands limp, clenching his fists only when abrupt changes in position were made.
>
> The proud mother now made it her business to present the new-born infant to her circle of acquaintances. First on the list came the chimpanzees, who had heralded the birth with shrill cries. Soon one of Achilla's human friends came to see her, and the baby was held to the wire netting to be duly admired. When my wife – for whom Achilla shows a marked affection – arrived, the mother gorilla, in her enthusiasm, tried to push the baby out to her through the netting. Achilla herself often studied the infant's tiny hands and feet and licked them carefully.

The second day after the birth, we saw the baby nursing for the first time. The mother lay in her tyre holding the baby close to one breast and then to the other. Suddenly, the youngster started an intensive search in the area of the armpit and finally found the teat. He fed to his heart's content, and Achilla seemed to enjoy it too. From then on, the baby sucked whenever he was hungry.

Later on, Achilla tried to feed Jambo soup with the spoon that she herself had mastered. The results were more comical than nourishing; once she did manage to poke the loaded spoon at his mouth, but the next time she tried it, he turned his head and got an earful.

On the fifth day Achilla laid her son on the floor for the first time. He did not appreciate it at all and loudly expressed his resentment. Immediately, his mother cradled him in her arms. But she persisted in putting him down, and soon the baby became used to it.

No other anthropoid species is known to put down its young. Experience in zoological gardens has taught us that the very small chimpanzees or orang-utans simply cannot be put down because the grip habit is so marked. In order to separate a little orang-utan from its mother for weighing, for example, two people are needed to disengage the extremities. Probably since the gorillas live on the ground, the ability to grip has not such vital importance as for the tree-dwelling chimpanzees and orang-utans.

Two months after the birth, Achilla made a weighty decision and handed Jambo over to head keeper, Carl Stemmler-Morath, for the first time. . .

Stemmler-Morath, by exercising endless patience over the years, had succeeded in establishing a close relationship with Achilla based on mutual trust. On19 June, assured of her keeper's good intentions, Achilla offered Jambo for weighing. Exactly nine weeks old, he registered 2.7 kg (approximately 6 lb).

At eleven weeks, well into his teething period, the infant showed an active interest in solid food, and would stretch out a hand for pieces of fruit whilst lying in Stemmler's lap. A week later, Jambo was making determined efforts to stand, using any conveniently close object with which to pull himself up.

Over the next year, Jambo learned to walk and cut his milk teeth, and after about eighteen months rarely suckled his mother, preferring solid food. All the time the patient Achilla continued to be an attentive mother and maintained a keen awareness of her infant's progress. On occasions, she was seen to encourage Jambo to become more independent. She began by putting him down, then backing away as soon as he stumbled towards her. She would then hold out a

hand to him, but each time he was about to reach her she would again move backwards. In this way, she managed to make Jambo walk the full length of the enclosure on all fours.

In her more playful moods Achilla, while lying on her back, would often swing her youngster to and fro above her head, while holding one of Jambo's tiny hands in each of her own in a firm, but gentle, grip. Jambo seemed to thoroughly enjoy himself.

The young male's general health and physical development continued to be successfully monitored by both mother and keeper, and two 'primates' closest to him during his early life. However, towards the end of his weaning period a minor problem arose when, at about two years of age, Jambo for some reason developed an aversion to being weighed. It seemed that he did not like the unstable feeling of the apparatus.

To overcome this difficulty, Stemmler-Morath encouraged the affable Achilla to gather up her reluctant son and mount the scales, where he duly recorded their combined weights and deducted Achilla's from the total. Achilla, who was not a particularly large female weighed 72 kgs (160 lb), which meant that, as a two-year-old, Jambo was very light for his age, weighing only 11 kg (26 lb). Despite this, Jambo thrived, and further weights obtained using the same method soon indicated a healthy improvement.

Once fully weaned, Jambo was introduced to Cathy, a female approximately one year older, with whom he had already established a tentative 'through the bars' relationship. Despite being a boisterous 14 kg (31 lb) male with a confidence to match, Jambo was frequently seen being carried around on Cathy's back, an interaction that rapidly strengthened the growing bond between them.

A short while later, the two were joined by a young male named Pepe and Jambo's hand-reared sister, Goma. The four youngsters quickly proved to be compatible and their day-to-day antics soon became a major source of entertainment for visitors to the Basle Zoo – they also formed the basis of the group in which Jambo was to remain until his eventual transfer to Jersey.

BREEDING AND SOME INTEGRATION

The first entry on Jambo's Jersey record card reads: 'M.293, Jambo – male western lowland gorilla, arrived 2 p.m. on Thursday 27th April, 1972 from the Basle Zoological Gardens. Released into gorilla house. Condition excellent!'

Three days later, the new gorilla house, designed to house a small breeding group, was officially opened by the highly accomplished film actor, David Niven. Some weeks earlier, Mr Niven had been tentatively invited by Mr Durrell to, among other things, act as best man at a gorilla wedding. In due course, a telegram arrived, reading, 'Delighted to officiate at gorilla wedding on condition I am at no time left alone with the happy couple – David Niven.' Now, armed with an appropriate and rather attractive bouquet of celery, leeks, cabbage, cauliflowers and curly kale, the debonair Mr Niven, internationally regarded as the quintessential Englishman, delivered a speech of immense charm and humour and declared the new enclosure open.

The initial gorilla introduction also went surprisingly smoothly, though while Nandi clearly found the new male very much to her liking, N'pongo eyed him with a great deal of suspicion and, for the most part, kept her distance. The unpredictability of the females over the ensuing weeks was to keep Jambo on his toes: so much so, in fact, that a short time later came this entry on his behaviour card: 'Jambo managed to leap onto the top of the surrounding wall of his area, he then had a brief walk-about on the roof of the building, before dropping back in again. The steel climbing frames in the outside enclosure have since been sawn in half. . .'

Jambo had been registered as a proven breeding male approximately one year before leaving Switzerland – his first offspring, a male named Tam Tam, was born to Goma on 2 May 1971. A little over two years later he again proved his worth when the first of his Jersey progeny, Assumbo, also male, was produced by fourteen-year-old Nandi during the early hours of 15 July 1973, after a prolonged labour of nine hours and twenty minutes. This significant and widely publicized event marked the beginning of what was to be a highly successful breeding programme for the Trust.

In October, N'pongo gave birth to Mamfe, a half-brother to Assumbo, who also became his close and valuable companion as, unfortunately, both infants had to be removed for hand-rearing. Nevertheless, it was an encouraging start, especially as Jambo's early relationship with his new females had proved far from satisfactory, because the temperamental N'pongo tended to overreact to the young male's sometimes rather clumsy displays of dominance.

Senior to Nandi by about two years, N'pongo had arrived at the zoo in 1959 when just two and a half years of age, and had fittingly spent the first few weeks in the guest room of the manor house, under the expert care of Gerald Durrell. Understandably, there was no shortage of volunteers ready to tend to her various needs and her subsequent transformation from a timid orphan to a confident, healthy and often mischievous youngster was complete long before Nandi's arrival in 1961. During the pre-Jambo years, a strong bond had developed between the females, although N'pongo was used to having things her own way.

So it was that in contrast to Nandi's immediate acceptance of Jambo, the older female refused to adopt a submissive role unless on heat. As a result of this, scuffles frequently occurred, during which Nandi, despite her obvious affection for the new male, invariably sided with N'pongo. This unfortunate situation, which may have contributed to the failure of both females to rear their first three infants, did little to enhance the prospect of establishing a true family group.

Despite successful matings, N'pongo's resentment of Jambo continued to unsettle things. Nandi would prevent infants from suckling by pushing them off the nipple and then holding them either too high or too low on the chest, while N'pongo would simply lose interest in hers. Consequently, during a hectic three-year period the zoo's gorilla nursery became a regular hive of activity, with keepers often working long into the night caring for Assumbo, Mamfe, Zaire, Tatu, Bamenda and Kumba.

In charge of hand-rearing was the then ape section head, Jeremy Usher-Smith, whose limitless patience and perseverance were rewarded with a 100 per cent success rate. Understandably, Jeremy's young charges soon presented a major attraction, and for hundreds of summer visitors the 'gorilla romps', which took place daily on the lawns at the front of the 16th-century manor house, became the highlight of their day at the zoo.

So successful was the nursery group that, in 1977, the Zoological Society of London sent Salome, their first born, to complete her rearing in the company of Jambo's offspring. The move proved extremely beneficial to her, as many years later Salome herself was to demonstrate considerable maternal competence when rearing her own offspring.

In time, however, and despite the disappointment of a stillbirth for Nandi early in 1977, the maternal abilities of both Jersey's adult females were finally realized, when their next infants were born. The subsequent rearing of the males, N'gola and Kakinga, formed the all-important mother-infant unit around which the group integration programme was to develop.

Although the rivalry between Jambo and N'pongo continued to thwart the Trust's aim of creating a cohesive family group, the successful introduction of the less provocative Nandi, together with her son Kakinga, to Jambo was achieved in the latter part of 1979. By June the following year, N'gola was also being included in the mixings, which sometimes developed into riotous affairs, with both youngsters playfully pursuing their father by first clambering up and then sliding down the steep gradient of the outside enclosure.

The zoo now had a total of eight gorillas, including three of the six hand-reared individuals, two daughters of Nandi, namely Zaire and Bamenda, and another of N'pongo's sons, Tatu. Of the other three hand-reared males, Assumbo and Mamfe were sent to Twycross Zoo, and Kumba to Regent's Park. Since then and after several more moves, Assumbo now lives in Prague. Kumba, meanwhile, currently resides at Chessington Zoo.

In Jersey, it was very soon realized that the existing accommodation would not be at all adequate in the long-term. After some exceptional fund-raising, construction began on a new and more spacious gorilla complex designed to provide the type of captive environment where the Trust's collection could develop into a well-balanced social group.

About five months before the official opening in May 1981, the hand-reared trio were transferred from their enclosure next to the manor house to the recently completed indoor section of the gorilla breeding centre. This proved a relatively simple process, carrying or leading them by hand, until Zaire decided to scamper off and take up residence in a freshly planted clump of bamboo. After she had successfully managed to evade the clutches of several out-of-condition keepers, we tried the psychological approach. We simply turned our backs on her and disappeared into the new building, at which point, suddenly drained of all confidence at being left alone, she whimpered loudly and sprinted in behind us. Within hours, the new building echoed to the sounds of frenetic antics as the gorillas chased about in wild abandon, using every available inch of space.

Jambo's move to the new complex
On 23 May 1981, Jambo, Nandi and Kakinga joined the juveniles. It was a busy and often hectic day: both adults had to be sedated and

an extremely vocal Kakinga caught up in a blanket before being moved.

Jambo was the first to go. At about a quarter past nine in the morning, as he leaned on the window ledge of his old area and peered out at a group of photographers, a dart loaded with 160 mg of Sernylan was shot from a blow pipe into the back of his left leg. Surprisingly, this did not seem to bother him. He looked down casually at the offending missile, pulled it out and tossed it aside. Within ten minutes, however, he had fallen asleep and could be transferred to the new enclosure in the zoo van.

For the exercise, a scientific and medical team comprising veterinarians, anaesthetists, a dental surgeon, physiologists and biologists had assembled from Jersey, England, the United States of America and Canada. As both Jambo and Nandi had to be anaesthetized anyway, it was decided to give them a thorough examination. *(see page 40) With Jambo being one of the most prolific breeding males, it was also considered important to be able to compare the quality of his semen with that of other captive males around the world. The entire operation was recorded on film by BBC Television for their award-winning *40 Minutes* programme, as well as by other units from abroad.

Soon after midday, Jambo was left to recover under observation and attention turned to Nandi and Kakinga, who had to be restrained from his efforts to wake his drugged mother. On their arrival in the new building, Nandi was weighed and measured and given a complete medical check-up, while Kakinga accepted his first opportunity to meet his sisters, Zaire and Bamenda, and his half-brother, Tatu. By three o'clock, Nandi was sufficiently coordinated to demonstrate her displeasure at being separated from her son. Her hoots of frustration drew an immediate response from both Kakinga and Jambo, which resulted in mother and offspring being reunited a short time later. It took time for Jambo and Nandi to completely shake off the effects of the anaesthetic. Once they were fully recovered, however, an emotional reunion was to take priority over any serious investigation of their strange new environment.

The Gorilla Breeding Centre

As often happens, the new enclosure required some changes once the occupants had moved in. Zaire, Tatu and Bamenda, having quickly demolished the attractive stands of bamboo in the large outside area shortly after their arrival, had progressed to fusing the interior strip lights with the aid of pieces of twig by the time their father had moved in next door.

Jambo's examination of the building's interior was methodically thorough, with particular attention being paid to the ceiling. Within a few days, he had decided that the facia panels were not to his liking. So he went to work. Watching him prise loose with chisel-like fingers 2-cm ($^4/_5$ in) thick boards each measuring 46 cm (18 in) wide by 3.3 m (10 feet) long, whilst either balancing precariously on a rope or hanging by one mighty arm from a brachiation bar, I could not help but marvel at his strength and agility. Flying screws and nails pinged and twanged against the barwork, and the panels creaked and groaned as they loosened. Having freed a section, Jambo, instead of letting it clatter to the floor, would retain his hold on it, descend and carefully feed the plank to me under the bars. In his first few weeks, he managed to strip in excess of 60 metres (200 feet) of timber from the ceiling.

The confidence with which he had carried out this demolition had earlier been noticeably lacking, when he had first seen the vast expanse and more natural composition of his new outside enclosure. At 2.00 pm on Friday 29 May, the doors were opened to reveal a landscape of hills and gullies carpeted with a strange soft, green substance – grass! Having spent the greater part of his life in a concrete area a fraction of the size, Jambo was naturally rather apprehensive about venturing forth. Not so Nandi. Despite being equally unfamiliar with this new surface, the quiet little female, with Kakinga clinging tightly to her back, had confidently pushed past the reluctant silverback and trotted bravely out on to the nearest grassy slope. Encouraged by her example, Jambo eventually followed, but only as far as the edge of the concrete apron, only feet from the door opening. There he stood, quietly surveying his new domain, a spacious half acre of undulating terrain.

Despite modifications in the meantime, the basic shape and appearance of Jambo's home remain much the same now as they did that afternoon. The gorilla house itself, which measures 20.3 m x 8.5 m (60 ft x 20 ft) is mainly divided into two large exhibition areas, which the zoo visitor is able to view through eight large windows of multi-laminated, 43 mm ($1^5/_8$ in) thick, shatter-proof glass, from the comfort of a public gallery. Off-show are two smaller dens, connected to the left-hand exhibition area by means of a manually operated crush cage. Directly above this efficient device is a dual-purpose area, which can either be used to hold a gorilla or, with both doors open, to serve as an alternative overhead tunnel joining both back dens.

About a third of each exhibition area is taken up by three levels of terracing. Further exercise and resting apparatus has been provided by three suspended metal platforms of different dimensions, a cobweb of 44-mm (2 in) sisal rope, two scramble nets and an overhead grillework of brachiation bars. During the last two years, each area has been further enhanced by the installation of a shallow splash pool, which helps to maintain an acceptable humidity of approximately 65 per cent and, more recently, an artificial termite mound, or 'honey pot', for feeding purposes. Some three miles of underfloor heating keeps the temperature at around 22°C.

Three compressed-air-powered doors connect the gorilla house to the outside enclosure, at whose southeast end it stands. Just a few metres from the building, the Trust's landscape architect constructed a main undulating hillock which reaches its highest point in the centre of the area, from where it slopes steeply to a valley floor over

7.6 m (25 feet) below. A smaller hillock rises from the opposite side of the valley then runs gently down across the middle of the enclosure. At its northern end stand two connected ponds, each fed by a cascading waterfall.

To the west of the main hillock a timbered area has gradually been developed over the years. A number of log structures, including one that supports a heavy duty scramble net, now replace the two or three large tree trunks that were originally set into the ground. Interlaced with more sisal rope, the timberwork presents a veritable assault course, particularly beneficial to the younger and more athletic group members. A short distance from the net, a specially toughened plastic tube was recently earthed over in such a way as to form an effective play tunnel through one of the smaller mounds.

The main objective behind the landscaping has always been to create an environment of varied terrain, with different levels, thus introducing natural visual barriers and potential escape routes for any subordinate members of the family who wish to avoid physical confrontation. It works very well.

Finally, bearing in mind the fact that it is the animals themselves that usually dictate the changes, the original short-lived clumps of bamboo that suffered so at the playfully destructive hands of the terrible trio of Zaire, Bamenda and Tatu, have since been replaced and several young trees added. This time, however, each planting has been successfully protected with a 6000-volt electric fence which, because of its low ampage, is capable of producing no more than a severe tingling sensation when touched . . . though enough discomfort to discourage vandalism!

Whilst surveying this new domain of hill, rock, timber and water, Jambo, without warning, issued a series of hoots which culminated in a crescendo of barks that echoed across the enclosed landscape. Such rarely heard vocalizations seemed to denote his concern at suddenly being confronted by an enormous open space. In fact, for the next few days, despite managing several tentative excursions outside, he remained somewhat intimidated by the sheer size of his area and highly suspicious of the green stuff that covered it.

The following day, Saturday 30 May, saw the official opening of the gorilla breeding centre. To start the proceedings, Gerald Durrell mounted a rostrum and read out a telegram from the Trust Patron, Her Royal Highness Princess Anne:

I wish Jambo, his two wives and five, hopefully soon to become six, youngsters a happy and productive life in their new home. I am only sorry that the addition of a daughter to my own family has prevented me from being present, but I am sure Jambo and his family will understand. My congratulations to Gerald Durrell and all the staff of the Trust on this latest development and their continued excellent work in the preservation of our rare and precious species – Anne.

Then, before the large and umbrella-shrouded crowd, the Lieutenant-Governor of Jersey, General Sir Peter Whiteley, declared the centre open. Despite the awful weather, everyone then moved to a vantage point to watch the doors slide back, the waterfall begin to flow and, hopefully, the gorillas to emerge. Jambo's handsome head appeared briefly in the rain, turned towards the bedraggled group of spectators and then promptly withdrew. As before, it was left to Nandi, carrying Kakinga in the high dorsal travel position, to venture forth and, to the delight of the crowd, complete a full lap of the enclosure before rejoining the reluctant star of the show, who had watched intently her confident demonstration through a window from the comfort of his den.

Notes

Weights and certain physical dimensions of Jambo and Nandi, taken while under anaesthesia following the move to the new gorilla enclosure:

Parameter	Jambo	Nandi
Weight	160kg/352lb	62kg/136lb
Chest Girth	131cm/54½"	102kg/42½"
Waist Girth	115cm/48"	83cm/34½"
Right Arm		
Length of Upper	44cm/18"	30cm/12½"
Length of Fore	32cm/13"	28cm/11½"
Wrist Girth	34cm/14"	
Left Arm		
Length of Upper	42cm/17"	32cm/13"
Length of Fore	28cm/11½"	27cm/11"
Wrist Girth	34cm/14"	
Wrist - 3rd Finger Tip	32cm/13"	
Length of Upper Leg	52cm/22"	
Length of Lower Leg	44cm/18"	25/10/½"
Length of Foo	30cm/12½"	22cm/9"
Length of Spine	77cm/32"	

KUMI

In the meantime, N'pongo was enduring the latter stages of pregnancy and in no fit state to be moved. With her four-year-old son N'gola for company, she had been left in the old complex where, just after midday on Tuesday 23 June 1981, the twenty-four-year-old female delighted everyone by producing a healthy daughter, whom I named Kumi, the Swahili word for ten, as this was the tenth birth recorded at the Trust. Actual parturition was captured by the BBC.

Despite some mildly aggressive behaviour from a clearly jealous N'gola, N'pongo once again proved herself to be an exemplary mother, and quickly took to nursing her baby at regular intervals. Unfortunately, her envious son persisted in playing the *enfant terrible*, and so to distract him I decided to introduce the good-natured Bamenda each afternoon into an adjoining area, which meant carrying the 100-lb six-year-old back and forth daily between the old and new complexes.

N'gola and his older half-sister quickly took to one another, allowing N'pongo the freedom to focus her maternal attentions entirely on Kumi. After a few weeks, she and her two offspring were transferred to the new centre to join Nandi and Kakinga. For the first time, the Jersey gorillas were all housed together under the same roof.

By late summer, the hand-reared juveniles had been successfully merged with the mother and infant unit to form an entertaining group of eight, although for at least four hours a day Nandi and Kakinga were kept with Jambo. The silverback seemed quite content with this arrangement and he and the others soon settled down into a routine, which allowed them all to take full advantage of their new spacious environment.

While the adults went about their business in a comparatively relaxed fashion, the younger gorillas, not surprisingly, expended huge amounts of energy. Climbing the timber structures, performing acrobatics on the network of ropes, and play-chasing at considerable speed over the hills and down through the valleys, their activity levels soared. New play-behaviours were also demonstrated. Games with water, grass and mud were messily, but thoroughly, enjoyed in the immediate vicinity of the pond and waterfall, as was belly-sliding down the surrounding grassy slopes. The stocky Tatu was outstanding at this, and lost no time in sharing his suicidal tendencies with his keepers. If we were caught unawares during a play session, we soon found ourselves up-ended and being pulled rapidly downhill, usually by the ankles.

The juveniles, and Zaire in particular, also continued to display their prowess at exposing errors in architectural design to the extent that on one very busy Sunday afternoon in August she managed to scale the perimeter wall. This she achieved by simply clasping both sides of a squared-off concrete column, which jutted out close to the main building, with the insides of her arms and legs, and then effortlessly pushing and pulling her way to the top. The mischievous female then decided to make the most of her excursion and take in the picnic area and the zoo cafeteria. This adventurous move resulted in a number of gallant, though rather pale-faced, gentlemen fending off her attempts to deprive them and their families of an assortment of cakes and sandwiches. Outnumbered, the wily Zaire quickly turned her attentions to easier prey. Scurrying away from the crowds, she made a beeline for an elderly lady who was quietly enjoying her lunch by the lakeside, sipping her tea and tossing a few crumbs to the flotilla of waterfowl. Then, as she turned to replenish her plate, the poor soul found herself staring directly into the stern, dark countenance of a gorilla…and promptly fainted. Immediately, several vociferous visitors rushed to her aid, driving off the pilfering Zaire, then boldly standing guard until zoo staff arrived to lead the excited youngster back to the complex. The following morning, both sides of the column were angled off with cement to prevent further such escapades.

Sadly in September there came the news that Jambo's father Stephi had died at Basle Zoo. He was 32 years of age. Then in October of that year, I was granted six weeks leave to visit the Volcanoes National Park in Rwanda, central east Africa, where, thanks to Dr Sandy Harcourt, his wife Kelly, and sister Elizabeth, I was able to achieve a life-long ambition to see for myself the rare Mountain Gorilla in the wild.

It was a trip that I had been planning for more than a year, and one that I very nearly had to cancel when the boisterous Tatu, having taken exception to me leaving his den late one afternoon, bad-temperedly slammed shut the service door with one of his typical acrobatic drop kicks, trapping and breaking my hand in the process. Fortunately, the swelling went down rapidly with the aid of ice packs and hot wax, though I left for Africa sporting a rather natty white elastic bandage. However, after a few days in the field, this soon lost both its elasticity and conspicuous gleam, and subsequently became far more useful as a cleaning rag for my binoculars.

From the Karisoke Research Centre, a cluster of green-painted corrugated-tin cabins nestling some 3,000 metres (10,000 feet) up in a grassy clearing on the southern slopes of Mt Visoke, I spent many memorable days following and observing the incredible gorillas. My initial sighting of a free-living gorilla was not to be the long-anticipated confrontation with a silverback. Instead, quite unexpectedly, I was treated to the endearing antics of a much younger male as he clambered up and out of the confusion of lush vegetation by way of a lichen-festooned tree trunk. At a distance of some ten metres, he sat on a knobbly, mossy perch and studied me through bright eyes. His name as I later discovered was Shinda, and he was approximately four and a half years old. Though my companions were familiar faces to him, I was new and he appeared a little suspicious. In an attempt to reassure him, I tried to mimic the 'gorilla grumbles'

or DBVs – deep belch vocalizations – which were being so expertly delivered by the others as we approached. As if on cue, there came answering grumbles. Then glossy, black shapes began to appear all around us as Shinda's family, known for study purposes as Group Five, acknowledged our presence. It was an emotionally charged moment for me, surpassing all my wildest expectations. Yet despite feelings of great exhilaration, I remained outwardly calm, and savoured the experience.

Apparently, in August 1980, Shinda's mother, Marchessa, had died, and shortly afterwards the little male had taken to sharing the night nest of his father, the very dignified Beethoven. I shall always remember this grand old gentleman with great affection, having enjoyed the privilege of his excellent company one black and thundery afternoon, whilst sheltering as best I could from a torrential downpour of rain and hail.

I was crouched in an excavated hollow between the huge buttressed roots of a giant moss-covered Hagenia tree when the gentle silverback emerged through the sheets of grey murky water. He grumbled, I answered; then after a brief pause, he lowered his enormous bulk down against me. It was as though we had known one another for years. Immediately I could feel the heat from his powerful body seeping through my waterproofs, and I can remember hardly daring to breathe. Yet despite being trapped by his sheer size, I couldn't help a nervous smile, though I kept my eyes down and concentrated on the steady stream of droplets that fell from the rim of my bush hat. They landed on my cape, making regular plopping sounds, and then without warning there was Beethoven's huge knuckle brushing the very spot onto which they had fallen. Grumbling to himself, he continued to wipe away the miniature rivulets and seemed intrigued by the squeaky noise his thick wrinkled finger made on the wet rubber. Suddenly I wanted to laugh. I thought of the note I had received from Trust Secretary, Simon Hicks, a few days earlier requesting photographs for the newsletter. One of you with a silverback would be nice, he had joked. Will this do, Simon? I thought, smugly.

Although too short to allow for any in-depth study, my time with the mountain gorillas emphasized to me the importance of trying to establish a socially balanced and genetically viable group around Jambo. I returned to Jersey with new ideas for exchanging some of our zoo-born progeny with a view to improving the group's gene pool and overall sex ratio. Suddenly, however, such considerations seemed unimportant, when, for the first time, our breeding and integration successes were interrupted by tragedy.

On 28 November, an error on my part while operating the air-powered doors allowed Jambo to pull open the slide connecting his area to that of the females. He burst through, to be met by a startled, but defiant, N'pongo who, though no match for him physically, lunged at the silverback. They grappled furiously. Panic-stricken, I tore open the safety door and yelled at Jambo but my shouts were lost amidst the deafening uproar created by the battling gorillas. Had I been able to make myself heard, it would still have made little difference. These were two old adversaries who, having been apart for more than a year, were now intent on getting to grips with one another.

Powerful blows from Jambo sent N'pongo reeling backwards and caused wide-eyed little Kumi to squeak with alarm as she clung tightly to her mother's back. With teeth bared, the screaming female was quick to retaliate and struggled desperately to inflict bite wounds to Jambo's enormous hands and forearms. They careered around the enclosure for what seemed like an eternity until, finally, having backed N'pongo up on to one of the higher inside terraces, Jambo suddenly rammed into her with such force that five-month old Kumi lost her grip. She was thrown high into the air and then fell, twisting and turning, to land heavily on the concrete floor some three metres below. Her limbs moved feebly for a few seconds, and then were still.

Despite the continuing struggle between her parents, I couldn't take my eyes from her inert little body. I began shaking, shocked and angry. Suddenly I resented them both, I cursed the stupid door system, but most of all I despised myself for my incompetence. With all my so-called experience, I, who had always emphasized the need for caution when moving the gorillas around and operating the slides, was now entirely responsible for the death of one of my own gorillas, and one of the most important future members of the Jersey group. Kumi, N'pongo's first female offspring, could also well be her last; after all she was getting on in years as far as breeding was concerned. But the loss of Kumi simply as an individual whose character was just beginning to emerge was far more difficult for me to accept. Poor old N'pongo could not seem to understand. Watching her after her separation from Jambo, bewildered, licking her wounds and trying to coax some response from her lifeless offspring, was heartbreaking.

At the time, some people suggested that Jambo might have attacked N'pongo intentionally in order to get at the infant, possibly because neither having witnessed Kumi's birth nor having seen her

1. *(above)* Jambo investigates Levan Merritt
2. *(below)* Jambo and Levan Merritt are reunited 22 September 1986

4. (*above*) Jambo at 11years 5 months, when he first arrived at Jersey Zoo

3. (*above*) Jambo as an infant with his mother Achilla and keeper Carl Stemmler-Morath
5. (*below*) Nandi with Assumbo, just 8 hours old

6. A young N'Pongo with Mr Durrell in 1959

7. Jeremy Usher-Smith with four of his nursery group

8. Mamfe demonstrates the grasping reflex of an infant gorilla

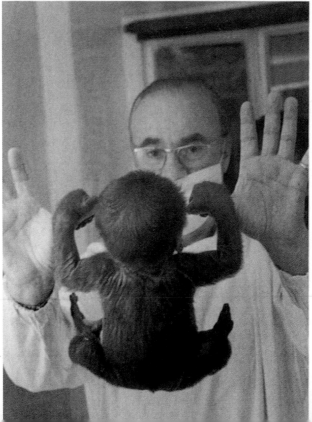

9. N'Pongo, biting the umbilical cord after giving birth to Kumba in 1976

10. Jambo playing with a latex block

11. Jambo under sedation

12. Jambo - still not entirely happy with grass under his feet - walks upright

13. N'Pongo with Kumi as N'Gola looks on in 1981

14. *(above)* With G-Ann
15. *(below)* A farewell party for Zaire and Bamenda 23 July 1984

before she was nearly three weeks old, he may not have considered her to be one of his offspring. It was a view that I was reluctant to share. Yet, data from field studies shows that infanticide is known to occur in the wild. If the silverback of a group dies and is replaced by another male, any young offspring remaining from the original male are often killed off by his successor. Though unpleasant and difficult to accept, this savage act does serve a purpose. Lactation in the nursing mother, which acts as an oestrual block, is quickly terminated and so her cycle is re-activated, thus bringing her back into breeding condition. In this way the new male is able to produce progeny of his own more quickly. However, I personally have no doubt that Jambo was intent on asserting dominance over N'pongo, and nothing more. He had certainly not attacked Kumi, though shortly before I managed to shut him off again, Jambo was seen to briefly carry his dead daughter around in his mouth, a strange gesture which prompted many people to believe that he had deliberately killed her – even the press.

N'pongo's attitude towards Jambo mellowed considerably after this tragedy and a few weeks later she was seen sitting close to the central interior partition watching and occasionally touching him through the bars. At other times, she tried to follow Nandi and Kakinga when they were let through to join the silverback.

N'pongo's Integration
In March 1983, N'pongo's oestrus – a monthly period of one to five days when the female is sexually receptive – heralded the beginning of her lengthy integration into the group. Although Jambo would probably again assert his dominance over her, I hoped that in view of her seemingly changed attitude she would accept it without antagonizing him too much. However, when the silverback began to stalk her menacingly around the outside enclosure, there was no denying the butterflies in my stomach.

Jambo was in no hurry. He seemed to know that eventually he

would catch up with his quarry and so kept his pace to a steady plod. N'pongo meanwhile, escorted by N'gola, appeared surprisingly calm, and stopped occasionally to pluck handfuls of grass to munch. For the most part she kept a wary eye on Jambo, though as the mixing progressed, it became increasingly obvious that it was only a question of time before he made contact. It happened very suddenly. While N'pongo browsed in the southwest corner of the enclosure, Jambo descended without warning from the top of a nearby slope. He cantered down at such a speed and angle that he simply ran into her, bowling her over and then dealing her a hefty blow across the back as she tried to rise. Immediately N'gola charged forward, screaming defiantly. Within seconds he had the close support of an equally vociferous Kakinga to bolster his courage, and together they confronted a rather bemused Jambo, who, after briefly fending off several of their rather absurd attempts to bite, finally chose to amble off with his two noisy offspring snatching and yapping at his heels. This unexpected behaviour from the two young males, combined with the more controlled reactions wisely exercised by N'pongo, eventually led to the senior female's successful reintroduction and subsequent mating – though not before almost 1,000 hours of closely monitored, nerve-wracking mixings had taken place over a six-month period.

MOVING ON

In the wild, it is usual for both males and females who have recently attained sexual maturity to leave their natal groups. Females will
generally transfer to other groups or perhaps join a lone male, while
emigrant males may form bachelor units or even travel alone for a
few years until joined by females with whom they may eventually
establish their own groups, thus reducing the risk of inbreeding and
minimizing the loss of genetic variation. For the same reasons the
movement of individuals between zoos is equally essential. In
August 1983, the first of several exchanges involving Jambo's offspring took place when his son Tatu was exported to the Oklahoma
City Zoo, in return for a four-year-old female named G-Ann, a
skinny little character with a passion for lettuce, whom I soon nick-
named Spider.

As an infant, G-Ann had sustained a broken jaw falling from her
mother during a serious squabble between the latter and another
female, and her injuries and subsequent treatment had necessitated
the youngster's hand-rearing. Her reintroduction some two years
later was fraught with problems: the last entry on her accompanying
record actually reads, 'G-Ann removed before Fredrika put her lights
out.'

Poor Spider. Despite her lack of years and slight appearance, she
received an intimidating full-blooded display from her patriarch-to-be
shortly after arriving. It was clear that the nervous little creature's integration was going to be a long and arduous undertaking. G-Ann was
socially inexperienced and found great difficulty in maintaining self-
control when being introduced to various group members. Her initial
mixing, with Zaire and Bamenda, took place on the grassy slopes of the
outside enclosures, under my supervision. All began quietly enough,
with the older females sniffing and touching the wide-eyed youngster

as she clung nervously around my shoulders. Gradually, however, as their curiosity increased, so the situation became more tense. Touches became deliberate pokes and pinches, and G-Ann's grunts of annoyance became more pronounced, while her grip on me tightened painfully.

When a resounding slap landed on G-Ann's back, she finally gave vent to her pent-up emotions. Screaming defiantly, she hit out at Zaire, which immediately gave a cunning Bamenda the opportunity to step in and grab her from behind. The near-hysterical G-Ann redirected her frustrated aggression my way and she promptly bit me, whilst simultaneously depositing a stream of fear-induced diarrhoea down my right leg and into my boot. For the next few hectic minutes the two sisters, thoroughly enjoying themselves, grabbed, pushed and prodded the vociferous newcomer. Trying to maintain my balance throughout all this, with one of G-Ann's arms drawn tightly round my throat while she swung the other like a club was, to say the least, not easy. After having been spun into my third pirouette, I decided to terminate the introduction and staggered back to the sanctuary of the back dens.

Though unavoidable, these early encounters did little to instil confidence in the young females and, for some time, G-Ann remained extremely wary. Then, quite unexpectedly, she found an ally in the most unlikely member of the Jersey group: N'pongo.

For several weeks, a connecting slide had been routinely left open just wide enough to allow N'gola to enter G-Ann's area at will. The six-year-old male, lacking confidence when separated from his mother, limited his early excursions through the doorway to rushing madly back and forth, occasionally grabbing at the newcomer in the process. G-Ann would snatch back in retaliation, but rarely ventured near the opening herself. Then one day, in a fit of bravado, she chased N'gola all the way through and suddenly found herself in the presence of the adult female. N'pongo simply looked down at her, which was enough to cause G-Ann to scream with fright and make a hasty retreat. However, within the hour, she was back, sitting just inside the adjacent den watching the doting mother as she meticulously groomed her offspring.

The following day, G-Ann was sitting close enough to be groomed herself, though this was not observed, and she spent most of a wet afternoon enjoying their company. Whereas the younger gorillas had refused to let her settle, the pregnant N'pongo was simply content to watch and occasionally acknowledge the nervous little female with the odd grunt or approving grumble. Under the control of his mother, N'gola's behaviour was also more to G-Ann's liking, as it allowed her time to explore new surroundings in comparative peace. A positive step towards her integration.

Meanwhile, a heavy and uncomfortable Nandi was rapidly approaching her parturition time. At 12.45pm on 23 December, she gave birth to her fifth live-born infant, a healthy and very vocal male. Along with several other staff members, I was fortunate enough to witness this marvellous event, which took place also in the presence of N'pongo, N'gola and Kakinga. Jambo also enjoyed an excellent view, as did Zaire, Bamenda and little G-Ann. Motaba, as the newborn was later called, became the first gorilla to be born in the new building, thus giving true meaning to its name of the gorilla breeding centre.

G-Ann continued to make a slow, steady progress within the group. She boldly tolerated a fair amount of teasing, only seeking out the reassuring presence of the stern-faced N'pongo whenever the situation got too tough.

On 4 March 1984, N'pongo marked her twenty-fifth year at the zoo by producing her sixth infant, another male, named Rafiki, which means 'friend' in Swahili. He was born in full view of the group, including his father, and his acceptance by the silverback was never in any doubt. The older brother, N'gola, however, had other ideas and pestered his mother repeatedly. His brattish behaviour became so disruptive that he had to be temporarily separated from N'pongo so undisturbed nursing could take place. In the end, everything worked out, because, as part of a long-term plan to try to establish a second gorilla family around an unrelated male with some of the Trust's younger females, N'gola was exchanged for Hobbit from the Zoologischer Garten Zurich, in Switzerland. He was the same age as N'gola, but had a larger physique.

In the meantime, however, Zaire and Bamenda, both candidates for the proposed new group, were themselves beginning to pose problems. Having attained sexual maturity, they had begun to solicit their father, whose enthusiastic responses introduced a risk of inbreeding. Subsequently, the two sisters were moved to reputable collections in England, Zaire to London, and Bamenda to Howletts Zoo in Kent, in return for a five-and-a-half-year-old female, Kishka. Having passed her medical, Kishka was first introduced into the Jersey group on 9 August. Almost without incident, she began to settle in with her new companions, including G-Ann, who by this time was clearly much happier.

Kishka had been born during the latter part of my time at Howletts, on 9 November 1978, and at three days old had spent twenty-four hours in my home while her mother was experiencing some problems with her lactation. There, I deposited her in the very capable hands of my wife, Jennifer, who some three years earlier had taken on the time-consuming hand-rearing of Kimba, Kishka's sister.

Throughout those Howletts years, our family was almost permanently extended by a host of exotic species, which mostly Jennifer, while strongly denying any natural affiliation with animals – 'I am not an animal person' – meticulously cared for. Consequently, endless sleepless nights saw fostering successes with chimpanzees, gorillas, honey badgers, monkeys – both New World and Old – and leopard, tiger and wolf cubs – all watched over by our very large and remarkably tolerant Alsatian named Rex. Amid such organized chaos, there was a stimulating upbringing for all. While our older children, Emma and Iain, happily shared their formative years with many Howletts' babies, so younger brother, Giles, was to become equally familiar with some of Jambo's offspring.

Kishka had responded enthusiastically to her pampering and needed little persuasion to greedily guzzle quantities of a very diluted human milk substitute. Fortunately, her mother, Shamba, was soon to resume near-normal lactation and Kishka eventually became the first mother-raised female at Howletts. Her upbringing undoubtedly contributed to the comparatively relaxed nature of her early mixings in Jersey, and by the time Hobbit arrived ten days later, she had firmly established a place for herself with the females and infants. Despite her lack of years, Kishka confidently adopted an 'aunt' role with N'pongo's infant, Rafiki, and was soon regularly cuddling and carrying him about.

Hobbit: the name conjures up images of a mischievous goblin-like figure, a description which could hardly have been applied to this stocky character, born on 2 March 1979 in the Stuttgart Zoologischer Garten, Germany. On 12 September, the young Hobbit strutted his way through his first mixing with the female group. Surprisingly, this and most other encounters went fairly well, considering the almost constant close proximity of Jambo in the adjoining exhibition area. Perhaps by this time the silverback was becoming used to the sight, sound and smell of new arrivals.

After a relatively short time at the Trust, he had gained a large number of admirers with his impressive physique and extremely expressive face. A typical Hobbit display would comprise a strutting trot with oversized feet directed slightly outward and shoulders widely spread, with powerful neck muscles rapidly manipulating his cannonball-shaped head from side to side. To complete the picture, his action would usually be accompanied by an almost continuous barrage of loud raspberry blowing which, though it may have detracted somewhat from his princely status, unquestionably added to his great charisma.

For his age, Hobbit was a big gorilla, weighing more than 60kg; I remain convinced that, when fully grown, he will comfortably top 200kg (400lb). Built as solid as Jersey granite, while at Jersey he also possessed an amazing turn of speed, which sometimes got the better of him, and he would literally run away with himself, crashing into things: the bars, the timberwork, wall and even other gorillas. I found him to be an intelligent and perceptive individual who missed very little, including the hanging grape and fig plants that adorn the perimeter wall, which are usually allowed to trail not more than half a metre down on the inside. While others in the group would show only a passing interest, Hobbit could frequently be seen jumping up to snatch at the meagre amounts of fruit. Then, early one evening, I happened to stroll around the corner of the gorilla building to see, in the distance, his familiar shape pirouetting as he clung by one arm to a substantial mass of vines. As he turned slowly round and round, the greenery became twisted into a strong, liana-like rope. I immediately grabbed some secateurs from the kitchen, raced down the length of the outside enclosure and began frantically hacking away at the tangle of growth just below the top of the wall. Hobbit's huge feet were about a metre off the ground when I finally severed his escape route. He dropped heavily back on to the grass, stared up at me for a few seconds then, clutching a large armful of cuttings, galloped off towards his den amid a fanfare of raspberries.

I never quite knew what to expect from Hobbit. Another afternoon, shortly after leaving his area, I was beckoned back by a chorus of raspberries to find Hobbit gently fingering a large toad. Having obviously found it outside, he had deposited it on the floor of his den and was curiously poking it. On seeing me at the door, he scooped up the startled creature and casually delivered it, with a flick of the wrist, in my direction. The luckless amphibian came spinning out under the doorframe and slid to a halt in the kitchen area, giddy but otherwise unscathed.

Hobbit also excelled in throwing other objects, which ranged from stones, clods of earth and pieces of wood, to softer items such as ripe fruit and, unfortunately, fecal matter. Although this behaviour was clearly designed to elicit a response from the public, Hobbit was not averse to also using his well-perfected underarm technique on the neighbouring Jambo.

Though initially intimidated by Jambo, Hobbit soon came to realize that he was safely out of harm's way while on the opposite side of the partition. So he began to take full advantage of the situation and frequently tested Jambo's patience by cheekily confronting him nose to nose, keeping pace with the silverback as he strutted, angry-faced, back and forth along the bars. Reciprocal bouts of wall-slapping and door-slamming would follow and then, as the tension mounted, chest-beating would begin. Time and time again, impressive hollow-sounding volleys could be heard, produced by powerful cupped hands trapping air against the naked skin of the chest. Having exhausted the novelty of such demonstration, Hobbit would suddenly discontinue his mirror imagery and hurl a concealed handful of something, usually unpleasant, at his extremely perturbed senior, and then disappear quickly into the back den blowing triumphantly through pursed lips.

It had never been the intention to run the two males together, as gorillas can be extremely aggressive animals and males competing over females in the wild have been known to sustain terrible injuries. Instead, it was hoped that Hobbit would have his own group, comprising the younger females, while Jambo would eventually be retired in the trusted company of Nandi and N'pongo and any offspring they might be rearing.

In the meantime, while living in the shadow of Jambo, Hobbit still had first to consolidate his position with the females and in particular those individuals who were most likely to become part of his family unit.

Motaba – A Royal Visit

The diary entry for Friday 5 October 1984 reads:

At approximately 10.40am, M940 Motaba managed to push his head up between the brachiation bars at the top of the right hand exhibition area. Though able to move his head freely along, and just above the level of the bars, he was suddenly unable to withdraw it downwards. . . On discovering this, he panicked and began to scream!

Jambo and Nandi initially reacted in much the same way a human parent might when faced with a similar problem. They climbed up, took hold of the struggling body and then gently tried to pull the then three-month-old Motaba free. When this failed and the screams, suddenly accompanied by a torrent of urine and diarrhoea, took on a higher pitch, Jambo became clearly agitated and redirected his change of mood towards the equally concerned Nandi, pushing her roughly aside. Then, once again, he tried to free his now-terrified offspring, only this time he pulled harder. The resulting crescendo of screams, which included bellows of desperation from Nandi, were suddenly drowned by a deafening roar of alarm from an extremely frustrated and angry father . . . but Motaba's head remained well and truly stuck.

To add to the drama, HRH The Princess Royal, patron of the Jersey Wildlife Preservation Trust, was due to visit the gorilla house in twenty minutes as part of the zoo's twenty-fifth anniversary celebrations. Unfortunately, it was raining and so the gorillas, instead of being viewed by the princess while enjoying their spacious outdoor enclosure, were to be seen inside.

Clearly there was no way that either parent was going to be enticed away to enable me to rescue the baby gorilla in any conventional way, so I clambered on to the roof and broke open the skylight above Motaba's head. In an instant, one of Jambo's arms shot up towards me, ramrod straight, and aimed instinctively in defence of his wailing son. Although, miraculously, he somehow failed to make contact, the suddenness of the silverback's lunge threw me over sideways. After picking myself up, I returned to peer down into the roof space. Jambo had managed to manoeuvre his son further along the barwork. Fortunately, however, Motaba was again positioned under a skylight and so I repeated my act of vandalism – only to be held at bay for a second time by Jambo's Herculean limb. He would not allow me near, and promptly gave vent to his feelings with warning cough grunts.

Meanwhile, the rain continued to hammer down, causing him to blink, though his face remained tight to the bars and he stared threateningly up towards me. What next? Well, all else had failed and so I resorted to talking to Jambo as he, now breathing heavily, began to experiment, testing the width between the brachiation tubes by gently sliding the whimpering Motaba one way and then the other, much like a curtain on a rail, but all the time being careful to support him from below, thus preventing strangulation.

Down to my right, a procession of bobbing umbrellas emerged through the downpour, while immediately below me, Jambo, ignoring my words of compassion, made a concerted effort to free his rapidly weakening offspring. Reduced to offering barely more than choked squeaks of protest, the little male grimaced visibly each time he was moved, and his large dewy eyes, having lost their sparkle, flickered open and closed. It was so agonizing to watch and feel utterly helpless, that in desperation, I decided to throw caution to the wind and grab him in the hope that I could pull him up and out before . . . but suddenly he was gone!

At a point midway between the skylights, where the gap between the bars was a few centimetres wider, Jambo had patiently recovered his trembling, suicidal son, only to have him instantly snatched from his grasp by a distraught Nandi. Reunited, the mother and infant huddled together, clutching one another in a mutually comforting embrace, completely ignoring the hero of the moment as he strutted around tight-lipped and bristling with emotion. It was disturbing to see Jambo so stressed, and I made a mental note to have the ceiling altered to prevent any repetition. Clearly we had been extremely fortunate not to have lost Motaba.

Meanwhile, the interior of the house, which a short time earlier had appeared not unlike a tropical arrangement from Kew Gardens, was now a complete shambles, and more closely resembled the aftermath of a tornado. Broken and flattened foliage splattered with copious amounts of fecal matter, induced through panic, was strewn everywhere. There was simply no time to clean it up – the royal guests had arrived.

Having ensured that Motaba had suffered no more than a severe fright, I hurriedly took my wet and bedraggled appearance out of one end of the public viewing area, as the royal party entered the other. Consequently, I never did hear exactly how Mr Durrell explained the 'jungle war zone' environment to Her Royal Highness!

On 23 November 1984, Kakinga, the gentle six-year-old male went on breeding-loan to the Calgary Zoo in Canada, making him the sixth successfully relocated Jersey-born gorilla, and the third to be sent abroad. It was also around this time that Kishka began to show a preference for the company of adults and especially that of Jambo, an interest clearly associated with the fact that her first oestrus had occurred soon after her arrival. Such pronounced sexual behaviour eventually led to a mixing with Jambo in December, during which mating was observed.

The First Grandoffspring

In 1985, two of Jambo's hand-reared sons, Mamfe and Tatu, sired offspring of their own, namely Asante and Ben, in their respective zoos, thus making the silverback and his female, N'pongo, grandparents for the first time. In Jersey, meanwhile, Kishka quickly assumed the position of third-ranking female, easily displacing the younger and inexperienced G-Ann. The previous December, she had been observed mating with Jambo, and now the confident young female conceived approximately one week before her seventh birthday. Understandably, the birth was eagerly awaited, for, if all went well, Jambo's group would have gained a third breeding female, thus improving its genetic diversity. Even as this countdown period approached, news of yet another grandoffspring arrived. This time it was N'gola who had proved himself by siring Zurich's first ever gorilla infant. Sadly, however, the male baby, named Moja, was to survive barely a year.

In the early hours of 14 July 1986, Kishka gave birth to a daughter, Sakina, whom she proceeded to cope with in truly expert fashion. On arriving that morning, I was treated to the sight of the new mother, with G-Ann in close attendance, gently examining her baby while relaxing in an enormous nest of woodwool, spread on the grass outside. At my approach, Kishka grumbled excitedly and interrupted her cleaning of the infant's face, hands and feet, to accept some pieces of fruit. Then, after a few sips of milk she turned her back and, emitting further grumbles, settled down and began to eat. By mid-morning she had allowed Sakina her first feed and, then, having patiently tolerated the natural curiosity of the other females and young, she carried her infant inside and up to the interior barred partition, where she deliberately showed her daughter to Jambo.

The following afternoon, acknowledged by a chorus of whines and grumbles from the excited females, Jambo rejoined his group. Without hesitation, and with her infant clutched protectively to her breast, Kishka approached and touched the strutting male in a typical submissive gesture. Almost at once, both adults signified their pleasure with reciprocal belch vocalizations. Then, shortly after a brief visual inspection of this, his twelfth Jersey-born offspring, Jambo moved off to forage, with a very contented and proud Kishka close behind. As is usually the case with nursing females in the wild, Kishka chose to spend the majority of her early days of motherhood in close proximity to her patriarch, instinctively seeking his protection, which clearly signified to me that her transfer was finally complete. Six weeks later, another youngster unexpectedly arrived – his name was Levan Merritt.

GENERATIONS

The next year, 1987, began sadly. On 3 January, Jambo's mother, Achilla, died at Basle Zoo at the age of thirty-nine. Europe's first breeding female gorilla had produced six children, including Jambo, twenty-three grandchildren and three great-grandchildren . . . and the latter two categories continue to grow steadily in number.

In the meantime, significant developments involving several of her grandchildren were taking place within the Jersey group, some of which proved a delight to observe, while others were more worrying.

The bond-strengthening interactions that now occurred with increasing frequency between Rafiki and Sakina, with the three-year-old male playing the protective big half-brother, proved both fascinating and often amusing to watch. To begin with, however, Sakina's mother Kishka discreetly monitored their movements, and remained strategically positioned at all times in case her assistance should suddenly be required.

Play invariably commenced with Rafiki parking himself directly alongside the ever-patient Kishka, from where he would entice the inquisitive bright-eyed infant to clamber clumsily on to his back or chest. Then, depending on her chosen position, he would either move off at a rate of knots in comical upright, bipedal fashion, clasping her to him, or pace importantly, Jambo-like, on all fours as she bobbed up and down clinging tightly onto his back whilst gazing vacantly about her.

Because Motaba spent most of his time, especially during the winter months, with Jambo and Nandi, the youngster had had far less exposure to Sakina. Consequently, when he first attempted to emulate Rafiki's behaviour, minor scuffles broke out between the two young males. Not surprisingly, the short-tempered reprimands delivered by their respective mothers had far greater effect than did the almost nonchalant reproaches offered by Jambo who, as a result, often found himself being playfully chased off by his offspring – something he was only too happy to go along with. The tumbling playful presence of progeny around the silverback became an increasingly common sight.

On the negative side, however, other intergroup relationships began to show the first signs of deterioration. Despite having enjoyed Hobbit's company early on, even the confident Kishka, since giving birth, had become wary of the fast-growing physical prowess of the sub-adult male. Physical contact between the two became less frequent and more tense. Hampered by her offspring, the young mother was soon unable to hold her own with the boisterous Hobbit, and fears for the infant's well-being became a concern. It was as if Hobbit truly resented Sakina.

G-Ann also seemed to sense the male's changes in mood. Often she found herself the recipient of redirected aggression, as Hobbit aired his frustrations at not being able to engage the likes of Kishka in a rough and tumble.

In spite of this, I began Spider's integration with Jambo on 6 May, the first day of her sexually receptive period for that particular month. For the duration of her four-day oestrus, she adopted an approach, retreat pattern of behaviour, throughout which the big male plodded patiently along in her wake. Only when within a few metres of her did he make his true intention obvious. Uttering excited high-pitched hoots, an indication of his sexual awareness, Jambo would bear down on the aroused but nervous female, only to be neatly side-stepped at the last minute. Avoiding the amorous advances of the silverback in this way, G-Ann gradually became a little more sure of herself and subsequently continued to run with the group in the presence of Jambo, even after her oestrus had passed.

On 1 June, excellent news came from Regent's Park. Zaire had given birth to a daughter called Kamili, which in Swahili means 'perfect'. Jambo's granddaughter quickly became a major attraction,

and for the first time in its 160-year history, London Zoo could boast a nursing gorilla mother.

Later that month, the Trust was informed of yet another gorilla loss at Zurich. The second of N'gola's offspring had been stillborn, though fortunately the mother, named Nache, had suffered no serious complications. Then on 1 July, better news stated that N'gola's third-ranking female, Inge, had produced a healthy full-term daughter, Neema, whom she was successfully taking care of.

Earlier in the year, N'pongo had recommenced cycling, approximately three years after having given birth to Rafiki. In August, Nandi also came back into breeding condition following a post-parturition period of almost four and a half years. Mating subsequently took place, though in N'pongo's case, not without some persistent attempts to interfere by Rafiki, whose unwavering determination to protect N'pongo eventually necessitated his temporary removal from the scene so that breeding could take place; Kishka, only too willing to comfort the sulking male, happily divided her attentions between Sakina and this, her adopted son.

Positive results using the very reliable Pregnosticon Planotest, a human pregnancy testing kit which also works particularly well with gorillas, were soon obtained from both females. N'pongo, it seemed, could be expected to give birth early in the New Year and Nandi a little later, possibly in May.

THE IMPORTANCE OF
BEING HLALA KAHILLI

The *Jersey Evening Post* article was entitled 'Introducing baby Hlala Kahilli!' and read:

> The most recent addition to the zoo's lowland gorilla colony is to be called Hlala Kahilli, thanks to the Lyme Regis Boys' Club.
>
> Her Swahili name, which roughly translated means 'Stay well and we will be thinking of you', is in keeping with the tradition of giving African names to all of the Trust's gorilla babies.
>
> The Boys' Club won the right to choose a name for her after they offered the highest bid of £250 in a charity auction which was held as part of the *Children in Need* Appeal.

N'pongo, at thirty-one years of age, had successfully given birth to her seventh infant on 23 January 1988, a worthy event to mark the Trust's twenty-fifth anniversary year. My one immediate concern – that the baby had arrived earlier than expected – was soon forgotten as I discovered the sex of the infant to be female. I was ecstatic! Then memories of Kumi came flooding back, and I made a silent vow that nothing was going to happen to this little mite, nothing.

Of course, things had changed dramatically since that fateful day, particularly the vastly improved relationship that now existed between Jambo and N'pongo. The silverback had readily accepted Rafiki, and I had no reason to think for one minute that Kahilli would be treated any differently. Nevertheless, I couldn't help worrying and I watched over her like a hawk.

N'pongo commenced to mother the new arrival in her usual competent way. She had completed the cleaning process long before being discovered with the baby and had, it seemed, consumed most of the placenta. Suckling had been seen and, though occasionally interrupted by a jealous Rafiki, who tried to share one feed by easing his sister off the nipple, there appeared to be adequate milk for Kahilli's needs. Once the usual enthusiastic investigations by the other females and offspring had subsided, N'pongo was left in peace to enjoy the warm wriggling presence of her latest newborn.

Kahilli's hands and feet were excessively mottled with the pink pigmentation not uncommonly seen on gorilla babies, which usually then darkens with age. However, at this early stage, her right foot sported three and a half bright pink toes, while the other had only two. There were also fingertips of the same startling colour, which gave the impression that this captivating little creature was wearing badly holed socks and gloves.

The following day all seemed well, but soon I began to worry about the lack of growth in the size of N'pongo's breasts, which should have been larger. Even after lengthy periods on the nipple, Kahilli would continue to search until falling asleep. Was she getting enough milk?

Over the next few days there was little change, so it was decided to commence a trial course of Syntocinon, a human preparation designed to stimulate milk flow, which was administered in the unusual form of a nasal spray. Not surprisingly, it met with N'pongo's sharp disapproval and soon became impossible to deliver with any accuracy, as the wily N'pongo was quick to cover up and hide her face behind a substantial forearm each time I approached. For the first time, hand-rearing became a possibility.

In the hope that such a drastic measure could be avoided, we sought a second opinion from our highly regarded local GP, Simon Slaffer, who suggested we consult a paediatrician, Dr Spratt, who in the past had been responsible for monitoring the health of a number of the Trust's gorilla babies. Having cast his experienced eye over the restless infant for several minutes, he informed us in his quiet, but confident bedside manner, that he strongly believed that Kahilli had been born three or four weeks premature, which in turn could possibly account for N'pongo's delayed lactation. Pointing out one or two wrinkles on the baby's belly, he commented, 'She's a little undernourished at this stage, but she's strong and active and should make this up very quickly; it's only a question of time.'

Dr Spratt was right. Towards the end of her second week, Kahilli at last began to draw sufficient quantities of milk from the now swollen breasts of her mother. Her whimpering ceased as both she and N'pongo were gradually transformed from a state of near misery and agitation to one of dual contentment.

This latest addition to the group produced some contrasting reactions from various other members. The young, but strongly maternal Kishka rarely left N'pongo's side, while her daughter Sakina, then approximately eighteen months old, took every conceivable opportunity to make contact with the infant. You could see that she longed for it to climb on to her so that she could carry it away.

Nandi paid her old comrade frequent visits and regularly checked on the scent and genitalia of the squirming offspring. Her equally inquisitive, though less confident son, Motaba, would emulate his mother, but quickly withdrew whenever the new arrival protested at being prodded by his clumsy leathery digit.

Surprisingly, G-Ann appeared to have mixed feelings about Kahilli's presence. At times she would simply sit quietly by watching N'pongo feed her baby, and on other occasions she would begin to harass the nursing mother playfully until vocally threatened, at which point she would then deliver a sneaky slap or half-kick to the older females before stomping off. However, whereas G-Ann's unpredictable ways could be interpreted as immature jealousy, Hobbit's displays were definitely of a more threatening nature.

Since his successful integration into the female and infant grouping, the young male had always exhibited a great deal of bravado, but mostly of the playful kind. So his bad-tempered response to seeing Kahilli for the first time was both worrying and totally unexpected. The first signs of his apparent resentment came as N'pongo entered the back den clutching her drowsy offspring. Suddenly, from an adjoining area, Hobbit coughed a threat, smashed both hands and feet on the partition with tremendous force and then spat several times at her. The situation required careful monitoring.

On 1 February, N'pongo and her infant, surrounded by an entourage of females and offspring, were joined outside by Jambo for the first time since Kahilli's birth. Prior to this, there had been numerous extremely encouraging interactions between the silverback and mother and baby through the bars. So it came as no real surprise when, within minutes of the introduction, friendly belch vocalizations from both adults quickly confirmed hopes of a successful unification. The usually so serious Jambo was clearly fascinated by his new daughter and also seemed pleased to have his old cantankerous female back in the ranks of his harem, and for a time he actually burbled his acknowledgment in almost uncontrollable fashion. His impressive group now boasted nine individuals.

LOST AND FOUND

My diary entry for Friday 20 May 1988 begins, 'M2. Nandi discovered at 07.45 with dead infant. Other females present, but not interfering – infant cleaned, coat dry, umbilical attached, placenta partially devoured. Very little blood, Nandi seems quite relaxed, coming straight over for a drink. . . .'

During my time as a keeper I have witnessed a number of births and seen many new-born gorillas shortly after parturition, but for me the thrill of discovery remains as strong . . . as does the bitter disappointment when confronted with such a tragic loss.

Nandi approached with her infant draped over her forearm. She grumbled in anticipation of her morning feed, and allowed me to inspect her lolling offspring while she ate. Burbling through mouthfuls of fruit, Nandi busily jogged her baby up and down, doubtless hoping for a life-giving cry, but sadly it was far too late for that.

Separating her off from the others was surprisingly easy, as when I opened the slides to the outside area they all piled through save for Motaba, who hesitated and looked to his mother to follow. Nandi, cuddling her infant high up on her chest, remained in her nest of woodwool next to the partition and Jambo also chose to stay inside, in the close proximity of his favourite female. Motaba now decided to forgo his mother's company and, after hovering momentarily by the doorway, joined the others outside.

Now watched only by the silverback, Nandi began to pace about on all fours with the lifeless infant carefully balanced across her neck. She tilted her head at an angle in order to keep the little body in place. Several times she stopped and sat with it pressed against her chest, quickly supporting the head whenever it flopped backwards. She also cleaned it further, paying meticulous attention to its tiny wrinkled face. Then, without emotion, she suddenly seemed resigned to his death and laid him down on to the floor. Slowly, she then trundled into the back den area to accept another drink, and I closed the slide down behind her. She turned, looked at the closed door, sniffed it, then drank and moved across to another slide, which led directly outside. I rolled an orange to her, which she gratefully accepted before stepping out to join the others. Having watched her disappear, Jambo soon followed.

Meanwhile, the situation regarding Hobbit had, by this time, worsened considerably, with his generally unpredictable behaviour towards the females and offspring resulting in him being isolated for long periods each day. N'pongo and Kishka, nursing young infants, were considered to be most at risk, and with Nandi first pregnant and then convalescing in a weakened condition, the only female fit and agile enough to partner the now 100 kg (220 lb) male was G-Ann. Though hardly a compatible pair, the two did occasionally engage in brief, frenetic rough and tumbles and games of tag, that is until the nimble Spider could make her escape.

Given that such irregular mixings with the flighty G-Ann were the best that Hobbit could hope for in the foreseeable future, it was reluctantly decided that he should be transferred to another suitable zoo park, one that could offer him the quality of life that he so deserved. He had matured rapidly and literally outgrown his place in the collection. To expect him to continue to exist in such an unsatisfactory way for a further twelve to eighteen months, which was when the Trust had hoped construction could begin on a second area, was unthinkable. This, coupled with his seemingly deep resentment of Sakina and Hlala Kahilli, led to enquiries being made internationally through the offices of the Species Survival Programme, an international body coordinating breeding programmes for endangered species worldwide. The National Zoo, Pretoria, replied that they desperately needed a younger male for their three adult females.

So it was that on 2 June 1988, Hobbit began his journey to South Africa. For the first leg of his trip he was transported to the mainland in an RAF Hercules. Much to the amazement of some onlooking airport staff, the departure of this much-loved character from the island of Jersey was signalled with a touch of humour. A near life-sized toy gorilla, which had earlier been presented by the Trust to the crew, was seen protruding and waving from the cockpit of the Hercules as it taxied out on to the take-off runway. Meanwhile, the real-life version, having been presented with a neatly packaged in-flight meal of apples and bananas, was munching away contentedly as we droned our way across the channel to RAF Northolt. From there, it was by road to Heathrow and finally in to the enormous hold of a Jumbo 747. As is often the case when exotic animals like this are transported, they tend to attract crowds of onlookers. The raspberry-blowing Hobbit soon had quite a following, including airport security guards, loaders, air crew and a few smartly dressed hostesses, all trying desperately to see just who or what was capable of making such incredible sounds!

Once safely installed in the bowels of the 747, I was allowed to give this still totally unruffled character a last drink and ensure that he had enough in his travel feeder bottle for the journey. As I added some extra bedding of shredded paper, Hobbit helped by tugging it through the bars, a game he had often indulged in back at the zoo, grumbling excitedly as he did so. It was difficult to believe just how relaxed he was. I said my farewells and, as I descended from the aircraft, I was treated to a reassuring tattoo of chest beats, accompanied by a trumpeting of magnificent echoing raspberries. Good old Hobbit!

Just over a year later, we received news that Hobbit had become a father, though sadly the female infant was found dead six days later with a fracture of the skull. Hobbit had nevertheless proved himself to be a worthy male. He had sired the first gorilla infant at the Pretoria Zoo and, judging by all accounts, could be expected to produce many more. On 23 August 1990, his second offspring was born.

RELATIONSHIPS

Despite varying considerably, Jambo's individual relationships with his females, in most cases, appeared to have little bearing on their respective positions within the group's hierarchical structure. One example of this was N'pongo's continued dominance over her contemporaries during the early years in spite of a poor standing with the silverback. However, if order of rank was dependent on the degree of affinity shared between the adult male and each of his wives, then Nandi should have been the undisputed matriarch.

While she, it seemed, had been totally besotted with the silverback virtually since his arrival, over the years Jambo had also developed an equally high regard for the portly little female. Nandi, with or without her offspring, remained the one who was clearly most comfortable in his presence and who, as a matter of routine, regularly shared the more privileged confines of his inside quarters.

Consequently, on 2 May 1989, when Nandi suddenly had to be sedated and temporarily removed from the group, Jambo was quick to display strong feelings of concern at her sudden absence. It was during the latter stages of what was to be her last pregnancy that such drastic measures became necessary. Following a stillbirth about a year earlier, Nandi had come back into oestrus and had been subsequently mated by Jambo in July and August. Calculating from her last observed oestrus, Nandi was now approximately 263 days into pregnancy. Other than having been mildly constipated for several days, a condition not at all uncommon at such a time, she appeared to be in good health.

By two o'clock that afternoon, she had stopped eating and was lying belly down in the outside enclosure exhibiting her usual signs of labour, touching her vulva area, smelling her fingers and periodically pushing or gripping the timber structures of the enclosure when straining.

Her intermittent contractions were accompanied by the passing of some blood. Otherwise she appeared to be restless but in no serious discomfort. However, some three hours after the onset of signs of labour, Nandi experienced two violent contractions and vomited several times. She then became progressively more quiet, and no further contractions were observed.

We decided to intervene, and tried to separate Nandi from the rest of the group, with only partial success, so I entered the outside enclosure to see how she was doing. At my appearance, Spider immediately thought it was playtime and stood upright, shaking her arms and grumbling in anticipation. Such was her determination to enjoy herself that I had to ply her with some treats in order to get closer to Nandi and then placate the others in the same way. Motaba, however, obviously concerned for his mother, shied away from my offer and remained at her side, his eyes full of suspicion as I crouched down next to her.

Nandi was breathing heavily and her rear end was saturated in blood. Then, as I stood to leave, she also tried to rise, but barely managed to push herself up on to all fours before collapsing again. Poor Nandi, she wasn't going anywhere. I hurriedly reported my findings to vet Tony Allchurch and then set about enticing the remainder of the group inside. Motaba was extremely reluctant to go, but with his mother now paying him little attention, he finally sought out the company of Rafiki and together they entered the house. Suddenly Jambo began to display. His favourite female was missing and, in anxious response, he emitted several penetrating alarm barks that were then taken up by N'pongo in the adjoining area. The others, meanwhile, clearly spooked by the vocalizations and the appearance of a number of extra keepers, milled about pushing and shoving for a place at a window which overlooked the outside enclosure, where Nandi was now being examined by veterinary staff. Although she was already in a collapsed state, Tony immobilized her with a jab in the back of her thigh, after which she was carried out of the enclosure and across to the vet complex. Her condition was poor, she was severely shocked, no radial pulses were palpable, and the mucous membranes were extremely pale. Emergency surgery in the form of a Caesarean section and partial hysterectomy had to be quickly undertaken by an expert team from the General Hospital. The final result was the removal of a lifeless male infant.

Without the prompt services so readily given by the highly skilled medical staff, Nandi would have died – a rupture of the uterus had caused massive blood loss. As it was, shortly after midnight she began to recover from the effects of the anaesthetic in the snug seclusion of the back den area of the gorilla house.

Earlier, the business of her return from the veterinary centre, though carefully screened from the others, had prompted the ever-alert Jambo into several strutting displays, each one noisily accompanied by a series of distinct hoots, which gradually turned into a slurred growling vocalization. Now, though still unable to see her, the adult male, on hearing the sounds of his awakening female, again acknowledged her presence. As I sat there with Nandi during the early hours, offering her small quantities of liquid, the groggy female made frequent attempts to croak a reply to Jambo's distant plaintive calls.

After two days, she had improved sufficiently to be allowed visual contact with Motaba, a move which offered at least some reassurance to her anxious offspring. Unfortunately, Nandi also began to show a keen interest in her sizeable abdominal wound. By midday she had managed to remove a number of stitches, thus necessitating her immediate return to the operating theatre where, once again, hospital staff were on hand to help.

Four days later, Nandi was well enough to receive Motaba and, not surprisingly, a quite touching and vocal reunion took place. While locked in a loving embrace, both mother and son comforted one another with choruses of off-key whines and moans. The following day Jambo was at last allowed both visual and tactile contact with his female and, though he swaggered into the adjoining area to impress her, within a few seconds he was observed affectionately mouthing Nandi's protruding fingers while returning her grumbles of pleasure and acceptance

On 15 May, Nandi was reintroduced into the group, and was quickly surrounded by an excited throng of females and offspring, all eager to touch and smell, all curious about the lingering medical odour of her now tightly stitched wound. Having weathered the wave of enthusiastic greetings and investigation, she trundled her way towards Jambo who, with legs and arms spread and eyes averted, stood on all fours a few metres away. Uttering a high pitched tremulous whine, she approached, submissively cowering when within his reach. Jambo, lips tucked and quivering with excitement, then allowed her touch contact, something usually reserved for playful offspring or sexually active females – now it was extended to a much-favoured companion. The tragic circumstances which led to Nandi's stressful separation from the silverback and his group had, if anything, served to strengthen the bond that had long existed between them.

Meanwhile, the equally close relationship of Nandi and N'pongo remained largely unaffected by the former's partnership with Jambo. Often these elderly females, who had shared one another's company for almost thirty years, could be seen quietly foraging together or simply spending time sitting side by side watching the latest of their boisterous progeny at play.

The years had mellowed the pair of them, and N'pongo in particular. No longer was she over-keen to intervene when squabbles erupted among the younger members, or even to reprimand her own offspring for snatching up more than their share when feeding with her. Yet there had been a time when she, more than any other, would have fiercely challenged all-comers, including Jambo himself, for first rights to feed. On entering her thirties N'pongo, it seemed, was happy to settle for the quiet life and, for the most part, she got on well with the new arrivals. Nandi, however, was less tolerant and frequently clashed with Kishka, although usually their confrontations tended to be more vocal than physical.

Kishka's progression through the female ranks had begun in the latter part of 1987, when her daughter Sakina was just over a year old and becoming more adventurous. Slightly less encumbered by her infant and never one to lack confidence, the young mother used various ways and means to ease herself on to an equal footing with N'pongo. Her gentle interactions with Hlala Kahilli, the occasional sharing of forage items – usually the less popular varieties – and the infrequent, though greatly appreciated, surrender of nesting material, were all craftily exercised to gain the trust of the old female. Nandi, meanwhile, would have none of it, which served only to fuel an ongoing rivalry. In a one-to-one situation, the younger female was able to displace either of her seniors, but if for any reason they chose to support one another, then Kishka would wisely concede.

Seemingly little affected by the general undercurrent of competition G-Ann, the youngest of Jambo's females, continued to go about her business in her own unique manner. In her case, there was often more to be gained by keeping a low profile. Though always a bit of an outsider as far as group life was concerned, G-Ann's quite remarkable and frequently unpredictable nature very soon made her one of the most popular gorillas in the collection.

Developed over the years, her fascinating repertoire of facial expressions and gestures, clearly designed to elicit a response mainly from the public, still prompts, with almost boring regularity, the question, 'Has she been taught sign language, by any chance?' The answer to that is a categorical 'No'. G-Ann's demonstrations include tapping the top of her head, pointing to her eyes, patting her open mouth with the palm of her hand and then pointing into it, and poking her tongue out at people. These are clearly forms of gestural communication, but although the messages behind some appear to be obvious, others remain a mystery.

Unfortunately, her somewhat off-beat behaviour did little to elevate her status in the eyes of the silverback. In fact, it was obvious that at times Jambo found her extremely irritating, and it appeared to be mainly for one very significant reason: this flighty little female continued to be sexually inhibited by his sheer presence, and subsequently failed to respond to any of his amorous advances. Although her cycle was often erratic, the occurrence of oestrus was still clearly recognizable by her pronounced behaviour of lip tucking and strutting. These outrageous solicitous presentations were usually performed from the safety of the opposite side of a partition, and yet were eagerly acknowledged by an aroused Jambo, but then it would all go sadly wrong. Once the pair were together, G-Ann's nerve would fail her and she would quickly resort to a well-practised evasive action routine, which basically amounted to her keeping a safe distance from the adult male whilst remaining available to flirt with him from long range.

During such tantalizing moments, Jambo would often demonstrate his frustration by adopting an extreme strut position whilst staring tight-lipped after her. Then, when unable to contain himself any longer, he would break into a prolonged series of hoot vocalizations, which he simultaneously accompanied with several tattoos of tension – releasing chest beats. Fortunately, this failure to consummate what can only be described as a virtual non-relationship seemed to have little overall effect on G-Ann's day-to-day life within the group, as once the odours of her four-day oestrus had disappeared, things would return to normal for another four weeks or so.

FAME

Considering the fragility of their relationship at the time, it was rather ironic that the BBC should request the services of Jambo and G-Ann to appear as a honeymoon couple in the popular television series created around the experiences of a zoo vet entitled *One by One*. In the story, Jambo played Albert, a resident male of a fictional zoo, who is awaiting a new female to replace his recently deceased mate. There he stood, a lonely but magnificently handsome silverback, a role which required no acting ability on his part whatsoever.

G-Ann's contribution, meanwhile, was to be more demanding, but having previously starred in a promotion for British Telecom earlier in the year, she took it all in her experienced stride. Though I had a walk-on part as a keeper, her performance as 'Susie' from the Jersey Zoo was mostly encouraged by her leading man, the highly accomplished character actor, James Ellis, who played an archetypal head-keeper named Paddy Reilly.

Being the true professional, his preparation for the sequences to be filmed in Jersey was meticulous. He politely asked for, and was immediately granted, permission to work alongside me on the section with a view to familiarizing himself with his leading lady, and vice versa. Initially, I did have some reservation about taking a total stranger in with her, but I need not have worried. His completely natural feeling for animals, enhanced by his gentle Irish brogue, immediately endeared him to the boisterous and sometimes impetuous seven year old.

Watching the almost effortless way he coaxed the best out of an intrigued Spider while at the same time delivering his lines with precise timing for one take after another was fascinating. A particular scene in which 'Susie' was supposed to feed 'Paddy' with a banana laced with tranquillizer actually involved getting G-Ann to remove a banana from his mouth, which she eventually did. Then the film was simply reversed very – clever stuff.

Though unusual for the Trust to allow its animals to be featured in such a way, the basic story of the series received its backing, as it endorsed the zoo's work. The completed episode proved extremely popular and prompted several concerned viewers to write in asking why Jambo had been sent to another zoo.

For the most part, Jambo's television appearances were confined to educational programmes such as *Wildlife on the Edge*, and for younger viewers *Dodo Club* with the excellent Sue Robbie. Yet he continued to provide the occasional cameo performance for drama productions, the best known of which was undoubtedly *Bergerac*. Several times in this series featuring the local police force, Jambo shared the screen with Jersey's then number-one human celebrity, actor John Nettles, alias Detective Sergeant Jim Bergerac. As if this was not enough, our majestic silverback, along with his entourage of females and offspring, was also filmed as a part of the backdrop for *Treasure Hunt*, *Blind Date* and, perhaps most unlikely of all, *Songs of Praise*.

Then there was the BBC's *Supersense*, a six-part series of scientific programmes which presented an intimate view of the sensory world of animals, an investigation of every sensory system – auditory, visual, tactile, chemical and even magnetic. The second of these excellent programmes dealt with sight and, to explain the workings of primate eyes, a crew from the BBC's Natural History Unit came to Jersey with the intention of producing sequences that they hoped would present a gorilla's eye-view of its family group. As this meant the camera had to be used within the enclosure, I was given the chance to operate a very expensive piece of photographic equipment whilst interacting with the likes of G-Ann and Kishka.

The eyes of both gorillas and humans have a field of view of 180°, and so to approximate this I was given a wide-angle lens, something the curious G-Ann found most interesting, especially as it was large enough for her to admire her own reflection in. Basically, all I was required to do was hold the pre-set camera at gorilla head height and play-chase first one female and then the other. Also involved were some hand-reared starlings, which G-Ann found even more fascinating! These birds, fully fledged and quite used to being handled, were being introduced to show what a starling's eye-view of a gorilla looked like.

As well as featuring in television drama, documentary and natural history programmes, Jambo was often the focus for photographic and film commercials, both for the zoo and the island. He featured in virtually every JWPT advertisement produced between 1972 and 1992, and appeared along with his extended family in many holiday brochures and tourism films about Jersey. One particular photograph taken by Phillip Coffey was used on the book cover for *The Thinking Ape*. Caught in a pensive mood, Jambo, with his chin resting on a huge hand, unknowingly emulated Rodin's *Thinker*.

In 1987, at the height of his fame, Jambo even helped to boost the sales of real Jersey Cream Fudge, but as the *Jersey Evening Post* article explained, he never actually tasted any:

> Poor old Jambo! Super hero, super dad and international media star he may be, but he can't have his cake and eat it! The lowland gorilla who shot to fame last year following the care he took with a young boy who fell into his territory, yesterday launched a new packaging of Jersey Cream Fudge depicting the Jersey Wildlife Preservation Trust, and marketed by Wilkinsons Confectionery Limited.
>
> But, because of his strict diet, Jambo is not allowed to have a sweet tooth, so after all the work of getting into the box he was rewarded with a piece of orange instead.
>
> Today is also a celebration for him because it is the first birthday of his twelfth offspring.

The anniversary of female Sakina's birth is particularly notable for the Trust because she is the first child of Kishka, who was also captive-bred, and this is the first time that a gorilla born in a zoo has successfully reared its own offspring, in Britain.

One of my favourite adverts for the Trust was, for a number of years, situated in the arrivals hall at Jersey Airport. It was a very large colour transparency showing the gorillas, with Jambo in the fore-ground, foraging contentedly on a sunsoaked afternoon in their spacious enclosure. It certainly caught the eye, and on various occa-sions whilst waiting to collect my luggage, I would overhear com-ments such as, 'That's the zoo where the little boy fell in and the gorillas saved him,' or 'That big one is Jambo, you know the one that does all the breeding!'

I always found it gratifying to hear people discussing my gorillas in such complimentary fashion, but then that was usually the way it was and, I am glad to say, continues to be. Whether I'm visiting the barber or the bank manager, gorillas invariably come into the con-versation. It was not at all unusual, when summoned by the latter, for me to first be asked about the well-being of Jambo and company, before a disdainful eye was cast over my accounts.

PATIENTS

Considering their close relationship to man, it is perhaps to be expected that the gorilla, with its many anatomical similarities, is equally, if not more susceptible, to the wide range of illnesses and diseases common to humans. Unfortunately, the effects on the anthropoids and other primates can be far more serious, and cases of pneumonia and gastroenteritis have been known to prove fatal. Consequently, in a captive situation where apes coexist closely with man, the risk of transmission is always present. Careful monitoring of the health of both keeper and charge is essential. At the Trust, any ape staff member feeling unwell is, for the benefit of the animals as much as for themselves, obliged to report sick immediately.

Keepers nursing coughs or colds are required to wear protective masks and disposable gloves when working around their animals and, in the event of their ailments developing into something more serious or becoming prolonged, they may be transferred temporarily to other duties.

However, despite such precautions, it is not unusual for any gorilla to contract at least one cold a year, and so suffer the miserable discomforts of sore throats, coughing, headaches and raised temperatures. Usually, once one starts sneezing, it is not long before the offending germs are passed on and the building echoes to sounds not uncommonly heard in the waiting room of a busy doctor's surgery. The basic treatments prescribed by local GPs tend, for the most part, to be the same or similar to those given to the ape. Syrups, powders and vapour rubs have all been used to good effect, though administering them has not always been so straightforward.

Naturally suspicious of new tastes and textures, even though their senses may be somewhat dulled by the presence of a heavy cold, the likes of Kishka and G-Ann will, with boring regularity, shy away from medication, especially if undisguised. Only considerable patience, some sweetening and perhaps a touch of bribery will finally win the day.

With Kishka, psychology can occasionally be brought to bear, with one of the most successful ploys being to convince the wary female that the medicinal mixture is intended for Sakina, by offering it to her always-eager-to-oblige daughter. Kishka, not to be outdone, has been known to greedily snatch and consume these mixtures before realizing their composition. Such cunning, however, can only be expected to have limited success before arousing suspicion, and is not a suitable strategy for use when more than one daily dose is required over a lengthy period of time. For this, there is no other choice but to resort to the wide range of proven taste combinations – one of the most unlikely I can remember is a foul-flavoured worming liquid being readily accepted in a cocktail of baby cereal, apricot flavoured I think, and velvet stout! Not quite what the doctor ordered, but it certainly worked. Experimenting with such mixtures, and sometimes even with the receptacles they are offered in, can tip the balance between refusal and acceptance. Of course, with the more serious cases of illness or physical injury where either specific amounts of antibiotic may be required or actual immobilization necessary, then the highly efficient blow pipe or dart gun automatic injection system can be utilized. In the meantime, trying to ease the discomfort of the more routine ailments continues to test the astuteness of mind of both human and non-human primate.

Of the latter, the finicky G-Ann remains by far the most difficult to deceive. Capable of being particularly stubborn over matters of taste, even when feeling off-colour, she invariably requires something different each time to overcome her suspicion. During one rather prolonged bout of communal coughing and wheezing, a particularly penetrating extra-strong expectorant had been prescribed to alleviate bronchial congestion. Surprisingly, most of the 'patients' had accepted this not entirely unpleasant syrup either straight from the spoon or mixed in with a drink. G-Ann tested it with the tip of her tongue and then clamped her mouth firmly shut. Typically, she had proved to be one of the more seriously affected and was having a painful time swallowing anything. Her eyes watered from the effort and she had a hacking cough. Despite her condition, she soaked up the extra attention and accepted a variety of foodstuffs and drinks . . . but refused medication.

Eventually, I decided not to disguise the syrup, but to demonstrate to her that it tasted good straight from the spoon. I should point out that I absolutely detest having to take anything like syrup, powders and tablets, and had planned only to pretend . . . but that was not good enough for G-Ann. We sat almost nose to nose, with her staring point blank at the spoon, and not so much as blinking until it came out empty. Despite the instant waves of nausea, I managed a gorilla-type grumble of enjoyment and then offered the same to my snuffling companion. She immediately swallowed her dose, grumbled contentedly and waited for more! Unfortunately she insisted that I set her a daily example and so, by the end of the week, when she was much improved, I was feeling decidedly queasy.

Some treatments, however, can be fun, as Rafiki discovered while suffering from a dry skin and coat condition. In addition to oral medication, more immediate relief for his hands and the cracked skin of his feet was a generous application of baby oil. These daily oilings developed into simply riotous affairs, in which we often both ended up as slippery as bars of wet soap. N'pongo's son also quickly discovered that the smooth fibreglass floors of the house made excellent slides for his lubricated hands and feet, and he soon attained startling speeds, much to the amusement of the public.

Being highly energetic and engaging frequently in rough play, young gorillas both in captivity and in the wild are more likely to incur accidental physical injury than older animals. In comparison with the other apes, the orang-utan, gibbon and chimpanzee, the gorilla is mainly terrestrial and as the juveniles and young adults of the species tend to climb most frequently, perhaps they should be expected to be more prone to accidents.

Falling from heights or being jumped upon account for a large number of cases of severe bruising or fracturing. Exercise ropes, though arguably essential, unquestionably present an element of risk. From my own keeping experiences, I know of two young gorillas who suffered injury, one fatal, on becoming entangled in ropes. The first, a two-year-old male named Djoum, sustained multiple fractures of the right foot whilst hanging upside down with his foot trapped in a tight loop. Fortunately, there was no permanent disablement, and he went on to become a very boisterous and powerful character. Sadly, the other was Kimba, a beautiful two-and-a-half year old, and a full sister to Kishka, who tragically died from strangulation.

In Jersey, Nandi's daughter, Bamenda, when about five years old, thrust her arm through a narrow feeding hatch and promptly got it stuck. Her companions, Zaire and Tatu, then quickly decided to take playful advantage of her predicament, with the result that the little female panicked and frantically wrenched herself free by throwing her entire body away from the barred grille with such force that she collided with the wall on the opposite side of the den. Crouched in a daze, she began to tremble and favour her left arm, and though she could still grip to some extent with her fingers, there was obvious pain from around the elbow. X-rays showed that she had suffered a backward dislocation of the elbow, which would require treatment under general anaesthetic.

Mr J Myles, the consultant orthopaedic surgeon from the General Hospital, quickly and easily reduced the dislocation. There was a pronounced sound and feel as the joint was reestablished, and the reduction appeared to be surprisingly stable. This was confirmed in the post-operative period, as even without any external support to the limb, recovery of use was rapid and without complication.

Bamenda was a model patient, accepting a course of mild pain killers without fuss, and making no serious attempt to exert too much strain on her injured arm until the swelling had subsided. Within a week of her operation, she was able to climb and swing about her enclosure using both arms, and a little under three weeks later was considered fit enough to be reunited with Zaire and Tatu.

Shortly after her fifth birthday, a lanky Sakina was seen to be nursing an injury to her left leg. Occasionally she would put some weight on it, though very gingerly and, at other times, she kept it off the ground altogether by using her arms as crutches. A closer look revealed some swelling, mainly around the ankle and, though she wasn't too keen, Sakina allowed me to manipulate the joint. It seemed likely that her lower leg was bruised and tender from either a knock or a sprain, and so it was decided to try some homeopathic medicine in the form of Arnica tablets. Disappointingly, there was little improvement over the next two weeks, which left no alternative but to sedate her so that a more thorough examination could be carried out. This proved straightforward enough, but the results were inconclusive. No breaks or fractures were detected, and her leg injury continued to be a mystery.

Throughout the remainder of the summer Sakina limped around, drawing oodles of sympathy from the public, to the point when I began to wonder if she was deliberately exaggerating her movements in order to gain extra attention. An increasing number of visitors had taken it upon themselves to slip the invalid an occasional treat in the form of a sweet or biscuit or something similar, and it was obvious that it wouldn't be too long before such a smart young female realized that she was on to a good thing. At times, Sakina was seen to exercise her left leg almost normally during play sessions with Kahilli, but then at other times, when foraging for example, she would revert, for no apparent reason, to limping. By late autumn, she was using her left leg fully again and though she had clearly experienced considerable discomfort early on, I still have my suspicions about her later behaviour!

Injuries sustained during fights, be they superficial scratches or deep canine punctures, will receive meticulous cleaning from the recipient or, in the case of a youngster, from the mother or perhaps even from an older sibling. Squabbles between adult females will invariably end up with both antagonists squatting an acceptable distance apart whilst closely examining themselves, fingering and licking their wounds. The broad forearms, having been used to shield-like effect, tend to bear the brunt of the damage which, fortunately, rarely exceeds minor laceration level.

Of course, wounds inflicted during incidents involving Jambo are occasionally more serious. A single deep gashing bite from jaws endowed with such incredible muscular strength would invariably warrant some veterinary attention. However, while seeming at times to have few pain receptors, gorillas do possess remarkable powers of healing, and often no more than close monitoring of an injury for signs of infection is required.

For health reasons, public feeding is strictly prohibited at the Trust. Sadly, despite warning notices, unauthorized feeding occurs fairly frequently, especially during the summer season, which causes vomiting and great physical discomfort among the gorillas. In addition, squabbles caused by such irresponsible behaviour, which, as well as disrupting group life, can also lead to injuries.

Litter or wrapped food items have proved to be even more detrimental to an animal's health, as Jambo discovered some years ago. An indication that something was wrong first came when he suddenly went off his food. While lethargic and clearly in pain, he seemed to be having difficulty in defaecating and so a lactulose solution was administered in small quantities of blackcurrant juice. Over the next few days, fecal samples were obtained, and on being examined eventually revealed what appeared to be pieces of clear polythene, some of which when unravelled were found to be the size of a large handkerchief – sandwich wrapping! I only wish that those responsible for subjecting him to such pain and discomfort could have witnessed for themselves Jambo's five days of utter misery.

However, despite such instances, a brief study of the entries in his medical file, or perhaps the noticeable lack of them, show the silverback to have enjoyed a comparatively illness-free existence, with barely a dozen pages of notes accounting for his residency of some two decades at the JWPT. Apart from a detailed and lengthy report on the very thorough examination that he underwent at the time of his transfer to the gorilla breeding centre, the records describe mostly minor ailments, the occasional stomach upset and the odd superficial wound.

DIET

Gorillas, like humans, differ greatly in size, shape, weight and temperament and, depending on their metabolism, individuals can be subsequently categorized as being either an ectomorph (slim, rangy) or endomorph (heavy, short in stature). While the latter group, which I call 'the storers', require a strictly controlled diet if obesity is not to become a problem, the more active 'burners' can be allowed more liberal amounts. For example, poor Nandi would only have to look at a banana to gain poundage, whereas the likes of N'pongo and G-Ann can gorge themselves – if allowed – without showing much of an increase in girth at all.

In the wild, a gorilla's bulk food diet includes items high in fibre such as stalks, roots, vines, bark, leaves, branches and shoots. With fruit-bearing plants, like the Batuna, which grow throughout the lowland forests of West Africa, they often prefer the stalk to the fruit itself, though gorillas inhabiting these parts are also known to include substantial amounts of fruit in their diet, to the degree that their jaws and grinding teeth are smaller than those of most East African populations.

Generally being selective and leisurely eaters, gorillas forage for food over lengthy periods, the reason for this long continuous feeding being the low nutritional value of their mainly herbivorous diet. Whereas in the wild the daily solid intake for a mature male like Jambo would amount to as much as 24 kg (60 lb), the staple items of his more nutritious captive diet add up to less than a quarter of the weight. Consequently, while the capacious stomachs and distended bellies which virtually touch the ground during quadrupedal locomotion are quite acceptable for free-living gorillas, such a physical shape in a zoo specimen would be considered extremely unhealthy.

All the Trust's gorillas receive a varied but carefully balanced diet of fruit and vegetables supplemented with a specially prepared 'ape pellet' containing vitamins, minerals and trace elements. Milk (freeze-dried skimmed milk) is offered twice daily, whilst brown bread and natural yoghurt with extra vitamin additives comprise a much-favoured part of their midday or late afternoon feeds. Hard-boiled eggs are also given once a week. As with many other species in the zoo, a sizeable percentage of the group's diet is supplied by the Trust's organic farm.

Each individual gorilla is fed a measured amount of the more quickly consumed high-calorie foods three times daily. Substantial amounts of forage in the form of freshly cut leaves and branches are also given. These provide necessary roughage, and also help to ensure that good healthy dentition is maintained. Varied with mixtures of seeds, nuts and occasionally dried fruit, forage is scattered around the enclosure, both inside and out, for the group to search for and then enjoy at their leisure.

Wheat straw or alfalfa given occasionally as forage is also used by some group members as extra nest-building material. As an additional treat, usually with one of the forage feeds, coconuts may occasionally be tossed whole into the enclosure for the gorillas to break open.

As well as being a much-favoured delicacy, a coconut, particularly for a young gorilla, can also be greatly enjoyed as a toy. Boisterous play sessions, closely resembling primitive forms of rugby football, are not uncommon following the introduction of several nuts into the enclosure. Gorillas competing for possession of, or throwing, catching, rolling, bouncing, and even attempting to juggle, coconuts are just some of the highly entertaining behaviours that have been observed.

For a number of years, this distribution of foods and forage had been one of the few reliable ways of encouraging the gorillas to work for their food. Another is the overhead feeding strategy usually employed during periods of inclement weather, which involves spreading food items on the false weld-mesh ceiling that covers the exhibition section of the house, so that the occupants then have to climb up in order to pull pieces through. More recently, the introduction of another feeding method, that of the artificial termite mounds, has proved to be of equally high occupational value, though it initially provoked a certain element of competitiveness amongst the ranks.

Installed in each of the exhibition areas, these partially hollowed-out concrete and fibreglass constructions, designed to test the manipulative skills of the gorillas, yield a tasty and often sticky reward to those excelling in patience and dexterity. In order to reach the contents, an individual is required to insert a suitably sized twig or sapling into the heart of the mound then, after a slight twist, withdraw it carefully with a small but highly prized quantity of either yoghurt, honey or perhaps peanut butter clinging to it – or maybe one of a number of other concoctions containing at least one of these ingredients.

Tool use amongst anthropoids had, in the past, always been more closely associated with the extrovert chimpanzee, in particular the use of sticks for fishing for termites, a fascinating behaviour first observed by Dr Jane Goodall many years ago during her extensive field studies of these remarkable apes. Since then, the introduction of artificial mounds has greatly enhanced behavioural enrichment for captive members of their species, as well as for the orang-utan and, to a lesser degree, the gorilla. Though introvert in comparison with the chimpanzee, the gorilla is no less perceptive and, as Jambo was quick to prove, the art of 'stick fishing', for such an astute member of a superior class of anthropoid, was easily accomplished.

When first confronted with the strange-looking perforated lump on his floor, he immediately climbed on to it and, while balanced on all fours, not unlike one of those unfortunate performing circus elephants on a ball, he proceeded to insert his fingers and toes into the

holes. Then, he carefully raised first each hand and then each foot up to meet his nose for an investigative sniff. Convinced that something pleasant and possibly edible lay just out of reach, he lowered his bulk to the ground, and casually reached out for a piece of forage, a willow stem, which I had deliberately placed nearby. This he trimmed neatly with his teeth and then pushed gently into one of the side openings on the mound. After a second or two, and with great concentration, he slowly removed it, gurgling with delight as a sample of the stodgy contents was revealed clinging to the stick's tip.

Jambo, in his prime, tipped the scales at a little under 180 kg, around 400lb, a healthy weight for his powerful frame, and slightly above average for a silverback. His height, on all fours, measured approximately 142 cm (56 in), while standing upright he attained just over 172 cm (about 70 in). For many years, the largest living specimen of *Gorilla g. gorilla* was the huge and ponderous Samson of Milwaukee Zoo, USA, whose maximum weight reached 277 kg (610lb). Phil, of St Louis, USA, who reigned briefly from 1941 to1958, is thought to have been the heaviest captive gorilla to date. His weight after his death was reported as being an incredible 353 kg (776 lb) and, even though this alleged recording was later seen to be an error, the later confirmed figure of 314 kg (690 lb) remains equally staggering.

For the majority of his mature adult life, Jambo was considered to be in fine physical condition, with his weight fluctuating mostly between 175 kg and 195 kg (385 lb and 430 lb) as he entered his thirties – a period of his life that, perhaps, could have been termed as his 'middle years' if his age was to be compared with the current longevity record set by Massa, a grand old male, late of the Philadelphia Zoo, USA, who died in 1984, a short time after his fifty-fourth birthday – the equivalent in human age to a remarkable 107 years.

According to David P Willoughby in his fascinating and very informative book, *All About Gorillas*, the mathematical formulae for determining the approximate corresponding ages in human and ape is derived from a study made of their respective ageing processes, as follows:

1) Ape's Age = 0.475 human's age + 3
2) Human Age = 2.1 ape's age - 6

a) Example:

Q If a human is seventy years old, what is the corresponding age in a gorilla?
A $0.475 \times 70 + 3 = 36.25$ years old

b) Example:

Q When Jambo was thirty-one years of age, what would the corresponding age in a human have been?
A $2.1 \times 31 - 6 = 59.1$ years

If the same formula is applied, the corresponding ages for Jambo's mature females in 1992 would be:

Name	Age	Corresponding Age for Human
N'pongo	35 years	67.5 years
Nandi	33 years	63.3 years
Kishka	14 years	23.4 years
G-Ann	13 years	21.3 years
Julia	11 years	17.1 years

FEEDING HABITS

Though by nature Jambo was a fairly amiable sort of character, he was also a creature of habit who, in his lordly position, required certain things to be just so. Where food and drink were concerned, he took second place to neither man nor beast, and would become extremely grumpy if kept waiting at meal times. He was also quite sensitive about the procedure of just how his feed should be administered. For some obscure reason, when being fed in his inside quarters, he preferred his fruit, and the apples in particular, to be placed directly into his hands, as opposed to being deposited on the metal feed tray attached to the barred service door. Failure to do this would invariably bring forth grunts of irritation.

He greatly enjoyed yoghurt, and it was not unusual for him to make his daily ration, containing a colourful assortment of vitamin additives, last as long as possible, much like a child with an ice cream. Like the other gorillas, his yoghurt was given in a paper cup and this he would gratefully accept, being extremely careful not to let it spill. Then, grumbling noisily, he would begin to eat by inserting an enormous index finger into the mixture, thus putting Archimedes' Principle into operation. The volume of yoghurt displaced was immediately slurped up as it overflowed, and the finger sucked loudly. Each little drop was savoured and, once the cup had been wiped around with the same leathery digit, and finally licked out with a large healthy pink tongue, it would be politely returned to me through the bars. His milk, however, he liked before anything else, and he was particularly fond of lumps. Lumps of milk powder that is, which had not been stirred in during preparation. These he would quickly remove from the surface with his lips before drinking one jug after another. Even the few seconds taken in refilling one of the 1.25-litre (2 pint) containers could prove to be sufficient cause for complaint from the big lad, who would voice his impatience with a rapid series of short, sharp cough grunts. Even so, once the milk had been poured and drinking was underway, those-bad tempered grunts would soon melt into drawn-out noisy slurps of pleasure. Then, in less time than it took to fill, the jug was emptied, and he would be grunting for another. Four jugs heartily consumed, Jambo, having shown his appreciation with several magnificently loud and echoing belches, would then clap his huge palms together, signalling that he was ready to eat.

During our intimate chats, which usually took place in the seclusion of a service area, I endeavoured to keep any direct eye-to-eye contact with Jambo to a minimum. A prolonged bout of staring is a form of threat to an adult gorilla, as it is to many other animals, including ourselves. However, there were times when Jambo would deliberately seek to catch my eye, usually when he desired something extra to eat. His ploy would be first to attract my attention and then stare at me with more of a pleading than challenging expression in his deep brown eyes. I have known him craftily to keep pace with me from within his walled enclosure, while maintaining a level, steady gaze in my direction in the hope that I eventually would give in and comply with his wishes. However, as extras are given primarily as rewards and begging is always discouraged, Jambo was rarely successful.

When the weather is favourable, the gorillas receive their midday meal of vegetables outside, the sheer size of the area providing each with ample space for comparatively peaceful communal feeding. Over the years, the various members of Jambo's extended family have always established places for themselves which, for the most part, allow visual contact with one another to be maintained throughout group feeding periods. Surprisingly, the one exception to this was the position favoured by the silverback himself. Jambo, it seemed, was quite content to be fed on the north side of the complex, out of sight of his females and offspring. However, being served first, as he always was, he did unfortunately have to suffer some light-fingered pilfering by certain of his progeny. Scurrying cheekily past to their own allocated feeding places, mischievous characters like Rafiki, Sakina and even the miniature Hlala Kahilli would boldly gather up any available food scattered around their patriarch. Whereas the juvenile male Rafiki, who should have known better, was occasionally scolded by his father, the two younger half-sisters never failed to take advantage of their sire's remarkably tolerant nature. Once Hlala Kahilli, having patiently watched Jambo munching a mouthful of greens, her nose at times almost touching his, suddenly snatched a much-favoured green pepper from his grasp only a split second before his massive jaws were about to close on it. Where did that go? The expression on his face said it all, but he simply resigned himself to the loss, and carried on with his meal. Though clearly entertaining to the public, such interaction, especially between two such extremes in size, more importantly emphasized the strong social bonds that existed within the Jersey Group.

Towards the end of one particular midday feeding session, Jambo, having been successful in protecting most of his meal from marauding offspring, grumbled contentedly to himself as he tidied up the remainder. Resting belly down, he was fully engrossed in the time-consuming task of plucking minute grains of corn and sunflower seeds from among the grass, and barely seemed to notice the arrival of a flock of starlings that were all too eager to assist him. The presence of wild birds, such as sparrow, starlings and even the odd seagull, is not uncommon in the gorilla enclosure, especially at feeding times, but on this particular day, there were literally hundreds of them. As their noisy numbers increased, so, inevitably, did the competition for food - Jambo's food!

A lazy sweep of the arm was a first indication that he was becoming a little agitated by the intruders who, in response to his gesture, simply fluttered out of reach, then realighted to resume their nodding search for seeds. Eventually, having swept the grass before him several more times with a huge hairy limb, but with no greater success, Jambo bided his time. Peering surreptitiously from beneath a beetling brow, he eyed an impudently close-hopping individual for a few seconds and then suddenly lunged forward. In a flash, his enormous hands closed around the luckless starling, while countless others rose like a dark, deafening cloud into the air. From within its leathery prison, the petrified fluttering bird could be heard protesting, its muffled squawks producing a few sympathetic aahs from the watching crowd. Jambo, though triumphant, could restrain himself for only a few seconds before investigating his prize, but as he peeped cautiously through his banana-sized fingers, a sharp protruding beak caused his large shaggy head to jerk comically backwards, a startled reaction that produced a few sniggers from his audience. However, undeterred and clearly intrigued by the rustlings within, Jambo quickly renewed his inspection. Gradually, the huge fingers began to spread, the beak poked menacingly out once more and Jambo ducked, hiding his face. Then a gap appeared and suddenly the starling was free.

'Well, I never,' said one elderly lady to her companion. 'Who would have thought of it?' Who indeed? Whether deliberate or accidental, the starling's release had, it seemed, won Jambo a few more admirers.

INTRUDERS

For the most part, Jambo seemed little affected by the crowds, which at certain times numbered thousands. Occasionally, however, his attention would focus on an individual whose very presence was, for some indefinable reason, sufficient to upset him. Clearly guided by instinct, he would promptly demonstrate his ill feelings with a warning display of lip-tucking and strutting, which he would then invariably round off with a very deliberate withering glare, accompanied by a volley of threatening cough grunts.

One such person appeared on an afternoon in the height of the summer season, a rather unsavoury character who was clearly the worse for drink. Having already succeeded in upsetting several members of the public and one or two of the gorillas with some unruly behaviour, he then tried to add injury to insult by throwing his whisky bottle into the enclosure. Although it bounced several times on the grass, it luckily did not break, and within seconds it had been snatched up by a furious Jambo and hurled back with incredible force in the direction of the drunkard. Few would agree that perhaps it was a good thing for the inebriate that it missed.

A regular visitor who continues to get a mixed reception from the group is the cat. Living close by, this predominantly white creature with the odd dark patch has, over the years, become increasingly familiar with the workings of the section. Ignoring months of 'Scat' and several none-too-gentle removals from the viewing area and kitchen the purring crawler has since wheedled her way in on an almost permanent basis. Yet one of her earliest appearances could well have been her last.

I was giving Jambo his early morning milk when the cat sneaked into the safety porch, the door being partly open as it was well before the public admittance time. Without hesitation, it coolly sprang over my crouched form and passed silently through the bars of the service door directly over the right shoulder of Jambo, whose startled response was far quicker than mine. His mouth full, he exploded into a choking roar, which saturated the pair of us with low-fat milk, then spun on his heel and chased after the feline as it disappeared like quicksilver through the slide opening to the outside enclosure. Cursing, I ran out and skirted the perimeter wall in time to see Jambo galloping at top speed a short distance behind the intruder, his crest nodding rapidly as he moved. On completing the best part of a lap, the cat suddenly darted to her left and took trembling refuge in the storm drain on the north side of the enclosure. Seconds later, the gasping silverback, still with flecks of milk splattered over his angry face, skidded to a halt in front of its barred grille. It was not unlike a scene from a *Tom and Jerry* cartoon.

As I bent over the wall to check on the situation, Jambo looked up. His chest was heaving and for a minute his angry, yet comical, expression was lost in the billowing clouds produced by his steamy, hot breath. For more than an hour he sat vigilant, refusing to be tempted back inside with even his favourite treats. Eventually, however, despite the attraction of the mewing prisoner, I wore him down with pleas and promises until finally he ambled back up to the house where he thirstily consumed an extra jug of milk and an early vitamin-fortified yoghurt.

I then returned to the drain and, after considerable coaxing, managed to extricate the sodden puss and promptly put her out of the zoo by the back gate. The following morning, during a five-minute respite in the cleaning routine, I looked down and there she was, purring and rubbing herself against my boots, behaving as if nothing had happened.

Prior to this, Jambo's only other experience with a cat, though not one of the domestic variety, had occurred some years earlier when one of the Trust's beautiful African servals decided to take a stroll around the grounds. Fortunately, it was still fairly early and the zoo was not due to open for another hour, which subsequently gave us time to locate and very carefully drive the nervous animal towards the nearest building, with a view to confining and netting it. From the direction it was heading, the most convenient place to corner this elusive creature was going to be the gorilla house, where Jambo and the group were contentedly foraging away. Emerging silently from some nearby shrubbery, the cat, attracted by the open doorway to the dimly lit public viewing area, promptly sought refuge and trotted gratefully in. All remained silent. Then, during the next few minutes, several things happened. First, my assistant at the time, the quick-thinking Phil Arnold, armed with a broom and a large plastic dustbin, ran to the far end of the building, entered the public area and hurriedly closed the door behind him. I, with catching net in hand, then completed the trap by nipping smartly in behind the serval and shutting the door behind me.

It was like the lull before the storm. Phil and I peered at one another from opposite ends of the viewing gallery. At first there was no sound, then all at once the gorillas reacted to the slinking feline presence. Giving vent to their surprise and alarm, they produced an eardrum-shattering explosion of noise. Jambo's mighty roars, combined with the barking screams of his females, were deafening, even from the other side of the glass. Clamouring at the windows, they hammered out their frustration and anger with tremendous force. The poor serval was terrified and ran up and along the wall to pass me. On coming to a dead-end at the doorway, he then turned tail and bolted back through my legs, streaked towards Phil and disappeared into the open-ended dustbin he had so expertly positioned on its side. The lid was slammed on, and the chase was over. It remains one of the neatest examples of animal catching that I have seen.

Meanwhile further adventures of the serval's self-assured domestic cousin have included more than one instance of her being accidentally confined to the outside enclosure – with the gorillas.

Unbeknown to me, this confident creature would sneak in during my early morning servicing of the area. Then, probably while too engrossed in either bird stalking or exploring to notice my exit, she would get left behind, resulting in a mixed exhibit.

The first time this happened, it was almost mid-afternoon before I was informed by a particularly sharp-eyed visitor, 'There's a cat in with your gorillas mate, did you know that?' 'Oh, she's in there again is she? She just has this thing about gorillas. Nothing to worry about. Thanks for letting me know.' From the depths of a sprawling bramble patch came a pitiful mewing which, advertised by the visitor's loud and informative comments on the chances of the cat's survival, very soon began to draw a crowd. This in turn attracted the inquisitive G-Ann who, on hearing the familiar sound, began to perform amusing gestures with her hands, while trying to make some sort of headway into the prickly thicket.

Revelling in the sudden attention created by his discovery, the visitor continued with a running commentary on the situation: 'This one will flush it out, and the others will catch it and probably kill it.' Moans of despair from the audience. 'Anyway, that's what they do in the wild,' he concluded. 'Someone ought to do something,' said one elderly cat-lover. 'Mmmmmm,' they all agreed, and continued to watch.

G-Ann, apart from being a natural clown, was by this time a fully grown and very powerful female, and more than capable of dispatching a cat. Even so, I was not unduly worried about her being a serious threat as, when confronted by an unusual situation for the first time, she tended to lose her nerve at the last minute and back down. On this occasion, her efforts to penetrate the brambles came to an abrupt halt when she suddenly got a thorn stuck in the sole of her right foot. Hopping quickly back on to the grass, she sat and raised her injured foot to the level of her nose and began closely examining it, but only for a few seconds, as the outpouring of laughter from the spectators suddenly goaded her back into action.

Angrily, she stomped off, only to return a short time later armed with a small branch, left over from the forage feed, with which she immediately began thrashing the offending brambles. Her violent blows only forced the cat to slink deeper into the tangled spread which, in turn, caused G-Ann's frustration to culminate in a deliberate and lightning-quick ejection of the stick, up and over the perimeter wall. 'Oooh,' gasped the crowd as they ducked their heads. 'Good job that wasn't the cat,' chimed in our expert.

Copied from the mischievous Hobbit, G-Ann's ability to hurl objects at speed, combined with an unnerving accuracy, as can be confirmed by many people, including one or two VIPs, has made it necessary for the Trust to display safety notices at intervals around the perimeter walls which read 'These animals are liable to throw things.' If G-Ann had her way, 'things' would very likely include cats!

Fortunately for this feline, she remained in the sanctuary of the bramble bush until long after I had brought the majority of the group in for their last feed of the day. Needless to say, G-Ann was reluctant to join them, but was eventually persuaded to do so when Rafiki threatened to consume her yoghurt. Then as soon as I opened the service door to the outside area, the liberated cat shot out like a rocket. However, the next day she was there, once again, back on duty patrolling the top of the perimeter wall and later padding silently along the exhibition area window ledges. With her nose pressed up against the glass, the irascible G-Ann eagerly followed her graceful progress, leaving me in no doubt that there would be further incidents involving these two.

When not chasing cats around outside, Spider liked nothing better than to be present when there was work to be done. Whether it was sweeping out the rain-water gulley, cleaning the ponds or cutting grass, she liked to be there. The spluttering noise of the motor mower engine did not seem to worry her at all, and she would happily walk upright tandem-fashion behind me, holding on to my

belt as I struggled to mow irregular-shaped pathways around the outside enclosure.

When working inside she was particularly fond of scrubbing, and would set to with great enthusiasm, lathering the patches of floor, wall or shelf. She loved the soap suds. Cleaning windows with G-Ann around was almost impossible, for no sooner had I cleaned and dried them she would promptly decorate them with large soapy handprints. However, as time went by and the handprints got progressively larger, the assisted cleaning sessions become less frequent. Finally, when brooms and hosepipes began to suffer with some regularity, and buckets were held to ransom, it was time to call it a day.

BRIBERY

During the course of a summer season, the number and variety of objects that manage to find their way into the gorilla enclosure are quite astounding. Some are deliberately thrown in, while others are accidently dropped over the wall by well-meaning members of the public who, in their enthusiasm to see the family group, lean over too far. Apart from general litter, items most frequently retrieved include camera lens caps, sun hats, combs, children's shoes and glasses. On one occasion, an observant visitor brought to my attention the shattered remains of a set of dentures – a loss no one ever reported.

Then there was the contact lens. I was called back one evening to look for this invisible object, which had fallen into shallow water in the surrounding drainage gulley, only to first receive a ticking off from its elderly female owner for taking nearly twenty minutes to arrive. The fact that I lived some four miles from the zoo and had been in the middle of dinner was clearly unimportant to her.

As is usual in the summer months, the gorillas had been left with overnight access to their outside enclosure. To make my task easier, I first tried to tempt them back inside. However, G-Ann, Kishka, Sakina and Rafiki, obviously enjoying the early evening air, chose to stay out and remain in close proximity to me throughout my search. Although there was very little chance of ever finding such a minute object, the irate visitor insisted on a close inspection being made of the puddles in the gully. Apparently, the contact lenses were not insured.

Full of curiosity, the gorillas watched intently as I carefully sieved through the silty water, constantly mistaking air bubbles for the elusive lens. Then after some ten minutes had elapsed, they lost interest and promptly made any further effort to search pointless by pushing me aside, and galloping one after the other back and forth along the gulley, splashing muddy water in all directions. Even if it had been insured, I doubt the lens would have been covered against being pulverized by the stomping feet of a group of playful gorillas. Anyway, their boisterous behaviour thoroughly soaked me and caused the visitor to depart hurriedly, voicing her disgust.

Although Jambo would have fared no better with the contact lens, he was, in fact, responsible for the recovery of a number of items of near equal delicacy, including several pairs of glasses. His willingness to partake in exchanges had first become evident many years before, when he began offering faecal samples through the bars in return for peanuts. As faecal sampling has always been carried out as part of a regular screening process designed to minimize parasitic infections, Jambo soon became quite accomplished at bartering.

From this humble beginning, not only did he progress to return-ing – for the right price – less offensive objects deposited by the public, he also perfected the art of throwing them up and over the twelve-and-a-half foot high wall of his enclosure. Jambo had been purposely encouraged to cooperate in this way, and I well remem-ber that the first pair of glasses to come into his possession belonged to yet another elderly lady, who was terribly apologetic for having dropped them over the wall.

On seeing that Jambo was sitting within arm's-reach of the undamaged spectacles, I explained to the lady that there might be a chance of getting them back, before any of the younger gorillas dis-covered them. I proceeded to try and rouse Jambo's interest in the idea of an exchange. First I dropped a peanut close to the spectacles and then pointed at them, whilst displaying more peanuts and call-ing to him. Chewing thoughtfully on the first peanut, Jambo immediately upped the price with one of his knowing looks. Then, having received a second, he craftily began fingering the spectacles while gazing up at the audience that had quickly gathered. Peanut number three produced the desired effect and Jambo, exercising quite remarkable dexterity, gently took hold of the frames of the glasses between massive fingers and, with a flick of his wrist, launched them upwards. Unfortunately, my catching ability was not equal to that of his throwing. Ten peanuts later, however, and at my fourth attempt, I caught them. The crowd cheered, the elderly lady hugged me in delight and Jambo, who had himself been close to giving up, ambled off for a bit of peace and quiet.

As he became more proficient at retrieving and exchanging, the silverback's willingness to cooperate soon extended to actually dispossessing any members of his group of any dropped or discarded pieces of human property that they may have come across. Usually his direct approach would be sufficient to encourage the surrender of whatever they had found, but sometimes a little more persuasion, such as a gentle nip or firm prod, would be required.

On being told on another occasion that 'Your big gorilla must have bad eyesight,' I knew that, once again, Jambo had taken possession of a pair of specs . . . this time sun glasses. An embarrassed couple approached, and the husband quickly explained that his glasses had simply fallen off when he had leaned over to look into the enclosure. So, adopting the now quite well-practised procedure, I threw Jambo a peanut, showed him others in my hand, and politely asked him for the glasses. With them already balanced on one of his broad palms, he simply thrust his arm skywards and sent them spiralling up and over the wall and, quite miraculously, into the clutches of the startled husband. 'I don't believe it! I simply don't believe it!' exclaimed his wife. 'How did he know to do that?' 'It's all done with bribery,' interrupted the man who had earlier made the sarcastic comment about Jambo's eyesight.

In addition to employing his bartering talents for exchange purposes Jambo could also, in the same way, be persuaded to perform simple but extremely useful routine tasks. One of these was to remove the heavy-duty plastic draught flaps when they became trapped in the slide openings, so that the doors could be fully closed. He was also not averse, for the right price, to cleaning out the runners of the various sliding doors in the complex. First he would remove any obvious pieces of woodwool, then, with the aid of a piece of twig, meticulously scrape the narrow channels free of any remaining debris, and he actually seemed to enjoy doing it.

The difference between Jambo's willingness to exchange and his cooperation to assist with such mundane tasks was that, with the latter, he would happily not accept a reward until completing the exercise, which in some cases could occupy up to several minutes of his time. But then, he always was a trusting sort of character.

16. *(above)* Giles with the gentle Bamenda 17. *(below)* Jambo chest-beating

18. *(above left)* Kishka with Sakina 1986
19. *(above right)* Hobbit
20. *(below)* G-Ann on set with James Ellis in *One by One*

21. *(left)* Jambo - The Thinker
22. *(right)* Jambo fudges the issue

23. *(above)* Massa at 54 years
24. *(below)* Jambo takes a stroll in the snow

25. (*above*) Jambo yawns disapprovingly at my failure to catch the glasses
26. (*below*) A rough and tumble with the boisterous Djoum at Howletts

27. With Julia

28. Jambo cele-
brates another
birthday

29. *(above)* Jambo on his 25th
30. *(below)* Nandi (Jambo's favourite female) with her last baby Motaba, in 1983

31. *(above)* Jambo quietly shares his forage with Asato
32. *(below)* Jambo in the adoring company of his offspring

COMINGS
AND GOINGS

Parting company with any of your charges is never easy, especially when the individual in question happens to be a particular favourite whose birth you have witnessed, and whose subsequent development you have observed with immense pleasure and satisfaction over the years. So, when the Royal Melbourne Zoo enquired about the possibility of obtaining a Jersey-born male for breeding, I found myself having to make the choice between Motaba and Rafiki. But then statistics really made the decision for me. Whereas all of Rafiki's four brothers had sired offspring, only Motaba's sister Zaire had, at that time, successfully reproduced so, genetically, it made more sense for the last of Nandi's progeny to be the one to travel down under. Late in March, I accompanied him on what must have been one of the longest journeys ever undertaken by a member of his species. However, he coped with it admirably and so after settling him in I left two weeks later, leaving Motaba in the capable hands of head keeper, Ulli Weiher. By all accounts, his integration into the Melbourne group, which already included an adult male, was not without its problems, but eventually it proved to be a great success.

As with earlier departures of group-reared offspring, Jambo was initially quite perplexed by the sudden disappearance of young Motaba. Nandi was also very disturbed and was seen sadly searching the entire complex for him towards the end of the day, uttering mournful cries that were then taken up by her mate.

Approximately two months later, the Trust acquired a third unrelated female, when the eight-and-a-half-year-old Julia, a gorilla with a much-publicized history, arrived from The Gambia.

Earlier in the year, the JWPT had been contacted by WWF (World Wide Fund for Nature) Netherlands, to see if there was a potential for re-socializing this solitary female by integrating her into Jambo's group. Accompanying the written request was a summary of Julia's background. In 1982, journalists working for a Dutch weekly smuggled the twelve to eighteen-month-old female into Belgium to prove that the trade in endangered species was prevalent at the time; from there they then took the little gorilla into the Netherlands, breaking Dutch law. Their action had served to encourage the Benelux countries to become party to the Washington Convention, and the journalists were approached by WWF Netherlands, together with representatives of the government, to help find an acceptable solution to Julia's future.

WWF Netherlands then became the official owners of the gorilla, who they decided could possibly become instrumental in establishing a pilot gorilla rehabilitation centre in Africa. In the meantime, the young female was sent to Eddy Brewer, director of the Abuko Nature Reserve in The Gambia, to provide her with a daily knowledge of natural habitat and climate.

During her time at the reserve, Julia progressed well. Each day she enjoyed lengthy excursions into the forest accompanied by her keeper – but completely free and able to climb trees and forage for leaves, bark, fruits and seeds. The only disadvantage of her otherwise idyllic life was the total absence of others of her own species, although she had been able to experience the company of young chimpanzees on a fairly frequent basis during her first five years. However, after having attained sexual maturity at about seven years of age, Julia clearly demonstrated her desire for a mate. Consequently, it was decided that it would be in the female's best interests to try to place her in a socially balanced group. If able to readjust to the tempo of gorilla life, it was hoped she could perhaps be encouraged to breed.

So it was on 21 May 1990, in the company of her devoted keeper, Karafa Badjie, that Julia arrived in Jersey to begin an inconvenient but compulsory six-month rabies quarantine period in the zoo's veterinary centre. As she stepped out of her crate grumbling excitedly, I immediately liked what I saw. Looking to be in excellent physical condition, she was of average build, weighed approximately 65 kg (144 lb), and seemed quite unperturbed by all the fuss. She also possessed a very appealing and expressive face which hid a mischievous, but probably inoffensive nature.

For an animal who had recently enjoyed the comparative freedom of regular exercise walks in the forest, Julia coped surprisingly well with her quarantine confinement. She kept herself busy and quickly proved to be an enthusiastic nest-builder and innovator.

Acclimatization was a chief concern and, in order to make it as gradual and as comfortable a process as possible, early summer had been purposely chosen as the most suitable time to receive her. This very soon turned out to be a wise decision, as she quickly showed a marked preference for the small outside run attached to her main heated quarters, and was reluctant to use the bedroom area on any regular basis. However, over the ensuing weeks, a routine was established whereby all food and drink was offered from inside, which eventually encouraged Julia to be more cooperative. Fortunately, her appetite had been unaffected by the long journey and change of environment and, there being many similarities between the Jersey diet and the fruits, vegetables and jungle fowl eggs that she had clearly thrived on in The Gambia, she readily consumed most items offered.

Over a three-week period, the quietly spoken Karafa gradually handed the day-to-day management of Julia over to me although, mainly for her benefit, he was careful to maintain an occasional presence. Often his deep, silky tones could be seen quickly dispelling any anxious moments that she may have been experiencing, and there was no question of where her affection lay. Consequently, following Karafa's departure in mid-June I noticed a change in her disposition. At first she became moody and appeared unsettled, but then her mischievous nature emerged, and she began to display an increasing amount of what can best be described as attention-seeking behaviour.

Servicing her area usually involved a rough and tumble during which the measure of her strength never failed to impress. I eventually discovered that the most effective form of exit from her area was to first tickle her into jelly-like submission, and then quickly slip out whilst she clutched herself with eyes screwed shut with ecstacy, giggling . . . not an easy manoeuvre in quarantine regulation astronaut-type garb. Most gorillas tend to be hypersensitive in the same areas of the anatomy as humans and fortunately Julia had particularly ticklish armpits and ribs, and was especially vulnerable under her chin.

In November, following a thorough medical examination Julia was transferred to the more spacious accommodation of the gorilla breeding centre. Though still effectively isolated from the other eight occupants of the building, she was able to familiarize herself with most of the complex and also, when her potential companions were outside, to observe them from windows in the exhibition area. Her initial reaction was a comical double take. She looked once, began to saunter off, then almost immediately returned to the window, where she visibly twitched with excitement whilst emitting deep belly grumbles indicating her pleasure. Such was her enthusiasm that she actually began tapping to them on the glass.

Quarantine restrictions were lifted on 21 November, from which point Julia was allowed regular visual and tactile contact via barred partitions with certain members of Jambo's group. Although understandably wary of their sudden close proximity, her reactions were for the most part encouraging. Subsequently, controlled mixings were organized in the off-show dens, with the interconnecting slides secured open just wide enough to allow the younger animals to pass through. Following a brief spell of reciprocal exploratory sniffing and touching, some nervously charged play interaction occurred. More often than not, it took the form of vigorous grappling, mouthing and some chase, retreat behaviour, which would then culminate in a stand-up slap and grab confrontation. Though rough at times, this was all good healthy stuff, and as sessions were increased both in frequency and duration, their interactions became less frenetic, and very gradually alliances began to emerge.

Meanwhile, Kishka and N'pongo, though very much intrigued by Julia to begin with, exhibited more concern for the welfare of their respective offspring during these boisterous affairs, and only bothered to approach the partition to vocally admonish the new female whenever she became over-enthusiastic in her attempts to play. In response to these threats, or to bullying displays from the boisterous Rafiki, Julia would retreat to the rear of her area, where she would proceed to rock back and forth while clutching armfuls of bedding material, accompanied by chimpanzee-like antics of lip smacking and gaping.

Despite the inevitable stresses associated with integrations, Julia, to her credit, remained a very approachable individual. Her play-interactions with me, though still rough at times, became more controlled, and this welcome change combined with her new-found confidence enabled me to leave her company without first having to tickle her armpits. Her mixings with Sakina and Hlala Kahilli continued to be successful and were incorporated into a routine devised to minimize disruption within the group. In addition, she was run in an area adjacent to all four adult females, including a suspicious Nandi and the inquisitive G-Ann.

By early December, Julia was confidently using all available inside space, and particularly enjoyed climbing and swinging about in the light and airy atmosphere of the exhibition areas. That same month, with Julia actively occupying the left-hand area, I decided to allow Jambo access to the right-hand side. Having displayed impressively some weeks earlier when Julia's face had suddenly appeared at a window, the silverback once again performed to intimidate. He entered in a shuffling, stiff-legged trot with lips tucked, stood rigid for a few seconds, and then shoulder-barged the barwork with shattering force, causing it to vibrate under the impact. He repeated this three times in rapid succession, and then stood glaring as Julia, in surprisingly bold fashion, beat her chest, lip smacked and strutted defiantly along the length of the partition. It was a demonstration for which Jambo seemed totally unprepared, and for several minutes he contented himself with pacing majestically around his section of the exhibit, quietly seething.

Inevitably, further goading by the female produced additional flurries of partition battering, which eventually had the desired effect, causing Julia to retire to the back dens. While her initial reactions could possibly have been attributed to a lack of social experience, it was noticeable that Jambo's overall response during this ninety-minute introductory period was also unexpectedly restrained. The following day, however, after similar behaviour from each individual, Julia chose to keep her distance from the bars and remained largely impassive, while Jambo went through his dominant display routine. Over the next few weeks, this became the pattern whenever the two were run side by side, which was as often as routine would allow, and though for most of the time Julia was generally relaxed, she was occasionally seen to comfort herself with brief bouts of rocking.

In January 1991, she was introduced to G-Ann in an hour which mostly comprised excitable, yet good-natured, bouts of sparring. Shortly before they were separated, G-Ann received a sharp reprimand from an anxious Julia for her persistence, in the form of a push and slap, and immediately responded by grabbing the younger female round the neck, causing her to scream. A scuffle then developed, with both gorillas cough-grunting and grappling furiously. G-Ann then retreated to the far side of the enclosure and sat down, only to be joined seconds later by a breathless Julia who made the simple, yet significant, gesture of playfully tossing a handful of straw over the head of her equally exhausted opponent.

After a two-month interruption when Julia was treated for some limb stiffness caused by shigellosis, she and Spider were run together daily from early April, and from their playful, boisterous and often comical interactions, it soon became apparent that a bond was beginning to form between these two misfits. Later the same month she met Nandi, too, in a comparatively uneventful encounter. Nevertheless, it was a confidence-boosting experience for the younger female, who was now beginning to assert herself a little more, while also learning to control her reactions towards those individuals who still intimidated her, namely the mischievous Rafiki and, of course, Jambo.

Until now, Julia had had little opportunity to familiarize herself with the outside enclosure, but as the weather improved, her access time to the outside was increased. Occasionally, she and G-Ann would be joined for short periods by Sakina and Hlala Kahilli, though the younger animals tended to lack confidence when out of visual contact with their mothers. Consequently, experimental mixings, first with the temperamental N'pongo, and later with Kishka, were put into operation. Neither female showed any real desire to impose themselves on Julia, and with wide-open grassy spaces offering greater flight distances, this stage of her integration proved something of an anticlimax, albeit a very welcome one.

Julia was, however, given a valuable lesson in the price of over-confidence by Nandi who, throughout most of a wet afternoon, patiently tolerated her clowning antics as she showed off to members of the public by swaggering directly in front of the exhibition windows, wearing a gaping grin, slapping the glass, and then actively climbing and swinging on ropes and bars. This in itself was reasonably acceptable, but not when carried out within a metre or so of the thirty-one-year-old female. Seemingly oblivious to Nandi's tense mood, Julia continued to perform but then made a serious misjudgment when she attempted to engage her senior in play by giving her a resounding slap across her back. Without warning, Nandi, with hair bristling, suddenly lunged forwards, grabbed the unsuspecting Julia and bundled her sumo-style over on to her side.

Following this, she then gave her a severe mouthing around the neck inflicting several minor abrasions before releasing her, clearly shaken and with her pride somewhat dented. However, despite such naivety, Julia continued to make steady progress and, by July, was running regularly with the female and infant grouping.

With Motaba apparently making good progress in Melbourne, thoughts had turned to a future destination for his disruptive half-brother Rafiki. Finding the right environment for him was not likely to be as straightforward. After all, he was at that time the youngest of five brothers, all of whom had themselves sired offspring. This subsequently made him a genetically well-represented individual whose removal from the international breeding programme would have little influence on effective population size. He would, in fact, be better suited for life, at least on a temporary basis, in a bachelor group.

Some two years earlier, at a meeting of the Anthropoid Ape Advisory Panel – an ad hoc committee set up in 1976 to further the long-term management of apes in captivity and to consolidate and coordinate research into their reproduction – I had first recommended a need to consider the forming of captive all-male groups, and their role as a possible solution for coping with the international surplus of zoo-born male offspring. Dr Sandy Harcourt supported my argument with an excellent paper emphasizing the important role that all-male groups serve in the wild, and how they could greatly benefit the captive situation. Unfortunately, our combined efforts met with a fairly negative response from the majority of UK zoo representatives.

Then, in June 1990 at the first Gorilla Workshop, I broached the subject with Ingrid Porton, the assistant curator of mammals/primates at the St Louis Zoo, who was responsible for initiating research into gorilla bachelor groups in the United States. Encouraged by her report on the St Louis males, and her willingness to consider Rafiki, I returned to Jersey with renewed enthusiasm. A short time later, an official request by the JWPT resulted in the St Louis Zoo agreeing to accept Rafiki on loan, some time in the summer of the following year. It was an exciting prospect, and a significant move.

In view of Rafaki's forthcoming departure, I had decided early on not to hamper Julia's integration with his direct inclusion. Even so, the lively Rafiki continued to capitalize on any opportunity that came his way to tease or intimidate her via a partition until the day before he left Jersey.

During his last full afternoon in the house, and purely for old times' sake, I gave the not-so-little monster access from the back dens into the kitchen area where, as a youngster, he used to play. Over the years, I have allowed a large number of the Jersey gorillas this liberty when they were young enough for their antics to be easily controllable. Mostly they comprised mischievous games with the buckets, or exploring the odd cupboard though, of course, they were not averse to helping themselves to an extra treat or two from the fruit rack, before scampering back into their dens.

So, on Rafaki's final afternoon, I prepared myself for the worst and opened the den door. Hlala Kahilli was the first to emerge and, quick to do the rounds, inspected all the exciting parts of the kitchen including my desk. Meanwhile, a rather hesitant older brother, perhaps surprised at being given access after so long to a favourite stamping ground, hovered in the doorway, but only for a few seconds. The fruit rack was virtually within his reach, and the temptation too great. He took two strides into the kitchen and immediately liberated a couple of oranges, which he began to devour noisily while scanning the room with wicked, twinkling eyes. Then, with his mouth crammed full with a mash of orange, he began to explore. Carefully and systematically, he half-lifted and peeked under the lids of a number of plastic dustbins that contained such things as seeds, nuts, ape pellets and, in the largest, milk powder. Suddenly, he had found what he wanted. The lid was cast aside, and a half-full paper sack of dried, skimmed-milk powder was effortlessly hoisted out. Hlala Kahilli, also with cheeks bulging, assisted as best she could, by bouncing the empty bin out of the way, so that they could make off into the den with their prize; which is exactly what they did, amidst a veritable explosion of snow-white powder.

Rafaki's mad, playful dash took him right through into the exhibition area, were he was confronted by a startled N'pongo. As they tore past her and around the enclosure, dragging the now very tattered sack behind them, both brother and sister began rapidly to change colour and, as the minutes ticked by, so the entire area took on a very definite Alpine appearance. Clouds of milk powder quickly settled everywhere, and the gorillas soon resembled snowmen – Abominable ones!

The following day, in a very contrasting atmosphere, Rafiki was crated via the squeeze cage and, like many of his group before him, was then moved up to the veterinary centre in readiness for an early departure the next morning. After a short flight to London Heathrow, where we unavoidably had to make an overnight stay, we took off for the USA. Due to the restrictions on the general import of primates into the United States, Rafiki was required to serve a compulsory thirty-day quarantine period in one of a limited number of approved zoos. Unfortunately, St Louis was not listed, which left Columbus, Ohio, as the most convenient destination. Rafiki took the journey in his stride, and was in far better shape than I when we eventually released him into the clinical confines of the new $2 million ultramodern Dr Joseph Cross Health Centre at around midnight, local time.

Later the following day, I said my goodbyes to him and left a rather subdued Rafiki in the very experienced and capable hands of the Columbus Zoo's great ape staff. My homeward journey included a brief stopover in St Louis, and so I took the opportunity to see for myself Rafaki's future home and potential companions, four individuals who made up the first captive all-male gorilla group – I wasn't disappointed.

ASATO ARRIVES

On 16 August 1991, the final and most crucial stage of Julia's integration started, when Jambo was let out to join her in the presence of the rest of the group. As expected, his entrance was impressive. He propelled himself out of the building at a startling pace. Lips tucked and hair bristling, he galloped up to the highest point in the enclosure and came to an abrupt halt. Breathing heavily, he surveyed the surrounding grassy slopes and gulleys from this commanding position, searching with a keen eye for his new female. Julia, having immediately retreated, paced hurriedly to the far end of the area, quickly moving out of sight of him.

A nervous chorus of submissive whines and grumbles mostly from the females, N'pongo, Nandi and Kishka, then prompted Jambo to display. He vocalized, emitting those familiar hoots, which gradually became more rapid and louder until they merged, whereupon he broke into a brief stiff-legged trot, before rising to deliver a series of penetrating 'pok-a-pok' chest beats. Dropping back on to all fours, he then concentrated on seeking out Julia. Excited by his presence, the majority of the group eagerly escorted the silverback as he moved majestically about the enclosure; G-Ann, however, remained in close proximity to his quarry, and was soon joined by Sakina and then Hlala Kahilli.

After approximately twenty minutes of patient stalking, Jambo managed to approach to within fifteen metres (50 feet) of this little band, before breaking into a charge which scattered them in all directions. The luckless Julia, unable to avoid his rush, was subsequently bowled over several times, though her screams brought an immediate response from the others, who courageously attacked the angry male with a barrage of slaps and bites. Kishka and N'pongo, attracted by the uproar, were also quick to add their vocal

121

support and, on being confronted in this way, Jambo chose to retreat a short distance, where he gathered himself and inspected his wounds.

The lure of the female soon led to a resumption of his search. Within fifteen minutes he had, once again, caught up with her, only to be forced back by the younger females, but not before he had bitten Julia on the right foot and she, in turn, had inflicted a similar injury to two fingers of his left hand. A few minutes later, while Jambo was preoccupied with fending off the bulk of his family, the breathless female was let back into the building after an introduction which had lasted just over an hour.

During the remainder of that month, a further twelve outdoor mixings were organized and, despite being subjected to more dominance-related displays by Jambo, Julia rarely showed a reluctance to be part of the group. In fact, more often than not, she was the first one out, and as she soon discovered, it was to her advantage to also be the first back in. Entering the house ahead of the rest of the group enabled her both to feed in peace, and lay claim to a generous share of nesting material. To help her achieve this, I had to attract her attention without the others noticing, and then devise a signal that she would associate with coming inside. I found that simply by showing her my keys and then walking directly up to the building, she would follow. Sometimes the keys would barely be in my hand before she was quietly up and sitting by a door waiting to enter.

The end of August saw a number of mixings in which no physical aggression at all between Jambo and Julia was seen. This, coupled with the fact that the young female had often been observed either foraging or playing within twenty metres or so of the patriarch was, at such an early stage of this final phase of her integration, extremely encouraging.

While Julia was gradually coming to terms with living with her own species so, on the other side of the Atlantic, Rafiki was also beginning to adapt to a new way of life. Having been transferred from Columbus to St Louis in the latter part of August, his integration had begun early the following month. By the time I arrived to observe his progress in September, things were well underway. The Jersey juvenile, having been exposed visually to all of the four males for an acceptable length of time, was already running on a fairly regular basis with the younger males, Rumple and Jabari.

Before my first two weeks had passed, Rafiki had gone a long way to consolidating his relationship with the younger males, and had been successfully introduced to Quito, a rangy ten-year-old from Boston. For me it was reminiscent of the early Julia and G-Ann mixings, though of a considerably rougher nature. After each stage, once a certain degree of compatibility had been achieved, the bachelor males were allowed access to a spacious and cleverly landscaped outdoor enclosure.

Following Rafiki's arrival, activity levels within the group had escalated greatly. Combined with the stifling summer temperatures, this resulted in some extremely hot and often breathless gorillas taking full advantage of the abundance of cool running water, and none more so than the unacclimatized newcomer.

During my last week, the keepers decided to go ahead with the final stage and introduce Leo, a powerful thirteen-year-old, who had originated from Los Angeles. As before, initial mixings were organized to take place inside, and it soon became evident that quite strong alliances were beginning to form between Rumple, Jabari, Quito and Rafiki. With the latter often boldly taking a leading role, the four teamed up against the senior male, retaliating like raging dervishes after each of his dominance-related rushes. United, they presented a formidable combination, which repeatedly took the edge off his confidence. By accounting for himself in this way, Rafiki emphasized to me the immense value of a social upbringing. Not only are the introduction of such individuals subsequently made easier but, in the long term, their companions also seem to benefit. In this case, it was agreed that the Jersey male's contribution had significantly improved the social dynamics of the bachelor unit.

At home, meanwhile, the pregnant N'pongo, having gradually attained the painfully large proportions of a barrage balloon, was entering into her countdown period. Despite her enormous bulk, she looked remarkably well and, accustomed as she was to the physical discomforts of pregnancy, the elderly female proceeded about her business in her usual unhurried fashion. As always, it was an exciting time and I began to relish the thought of discovering yet another gorilla infant or perhaps, once again, being lucky enough to witness the truly magical moment of birth.

As usual, it happened on my day off – and I had been so sure that nothing was going to take place until after the weekend. At approximately 5.30 pm on Sunday 20 October 1991, I received a telephone call informing me that 'N'pongo has started!' Before I could even leave for the zoo, a second call came through: 'She's had it!' It was as quick as that. Within minutes of commencing labour, the old girl, at the age of thirty-four, had effortlessly popped out her eighth offspring.

The birth had taken place in the left hand exhibition area, and was actually witnessed by a small, but privileged, number of visitors who had braved the elements on a very wet and blustery afternoon. Among the captivated audience was the highly accomplished comedy actor, John Cleese, who was so moved by what he saw that he later applied to pay for the privilege of adopting the baby. With the rain hammering down outside, the spectators continued to watch in hushed fascination as N'pongo, surrounded by a burbling throng of females and youngsters, began to examine her infant, a good-sized healthy male. Having meticulously cleaned away the birth fluids and embryonic membranes with much licking and wiping, she then proceeded to devour the placenta and most of the pale, rubbery umbilical cord.

Understandably, the squirming little body was the focus of attention and of particular interest to the younger females, Hlala Kahilli and Sakina, both of whom remained in immediate proximity throughout the mother's preliminary investigations and subsequent nursing of her baby. The curiosity of these two was such that, at times, their inquisitive expressions were poised barely inches from the newcomer who, oblivious to his audience, was already beginning to demonstrate the remarkably strong gripping ability of the new-born anthropoid ape. Eyes open, he flexed his wiry limbs and embarked on an unsteady, yet vigorous, search for the nipple.

From the adjoining area, Jambo quietly studied his latest progeny, whilst the ever-present Nandi peered from behind his massive frame to respond eagerly to the infant's mewing cries with deep belly grumbles. Her vocalizations were, in turn, answered enthusiastically by N'pongo who, accompanied by her entourage, shuffled across to be greeted at the partition amid a hum of excitement. A birth in any family is a major event and, as always, the Jersey group made the most of it, heralding the arrival of Asato, the Nigerian Ibo dialect word for 'eight', in typical gorilla style, with the attendant females jostling one another, hoping to steal a sniff or touch.

Once individual curiosities had been satisfied, albeit temporarily, N'pongo was allowed to reach the sanctuary of the back dens where, after taking some refreshment, she settled down and within a short time, breast-feeding was observed. As the grand old ex-matriarch reclined in her woodwool nest, Hlala Kahilli, with an almost comical expression of intense concentration on her face, watched closely as her new-born brother suckled away. The driving rain continued to rattle on the skylights above, and the other members of the group set about their ritualistic nest-building. This involved armfuls of bedding material being carefully arranged and then rearranged, sometimes several times over before satisfaction was achieved. Eventually the rustling subsided and soon all that could be heard was the sound of regular heavy breathing, punctuated by an occasional bout of scratching and the odd snuffling grunt.

Before quietly leaving the building that evening, I noticed that Hlala Kahilli, having already surreptitiously helped herself to a brief feed from her mother, lay sleeping with her right arm resting across Asato. Jealousy, affection or a mixture of both? Whatever the reason, the signs were that she was certainly going to be a strong influence in his upbringing.

'CHILDREN'

Children, particularly those of the Channel Islands, had always regarded Jambo as being a lovable celebrity. Whether visiting the zoo with their families, or as a part of an organized school or Dodo Club outing, youngsters of all ages flocked to see him. Often, amid their jostling, chattering crowds, some could be seen standing as if rooted to the spot, awe-struck by his immense size, while others, less intimidated, would encourage one another to clap and cheer whenever he made an appearance. They seemed drawn to him, and whatever their initial reaction may have been, it was clear that for the majority the experience of being able to observe first-hand such a large and powerful anthropoid as 'Old Jambo' was one that they hugely enjoyed, and probably would never forget as their expressions, often priceless, duly confirmed.

With school parties at the zoo alone exceeding some 8,000 children a year, and the Trust's Dodo Club junior membership for children up to sixteen amounting to almost half that number again, it was hardly surprising that Jambo's birthdays were generously acknowledged. Each year the number and variety of cards that arrived was always impressive.

On the occasion of his twenty-first birthday, the *Jersey Evening Post* published a congratulatory article and photographs. That same day, a group of school children, having congregated at the wall of the outside enclosure, unexpectedly burst into choruses of 'Happy birthday to you, Happy birthday dear Jambo . . .' The bemused silverback politely took a brief respite from the serious business of foraging to cast an appraising eye up at the row of happy adoring faces.

Jambo's twenty-fifth birthday was also celebrated in some style, with a 'gorilla-sized' cake being generously donated by a local baker. The cake, decorated with the appropriate king-sized numerals piped in bright red icing, had been carefully positioned for the press to take their photographs. However, almost before a shutter could click, the pastry chef's artistic masterpiece was nonchalantly flipped over face-down on the ground by a disinterested Jambo who, without so much as a backward glance, then ambled off in search of some real food, leaving his less fussy females to help themselves.

High profile animals such as the gorilla tend to be major attractions in any zoo. Such is their impact that they sometimes receive greater acclaim and recognition than many local public figures. The Jersey family is certainly no exception. Other events that have drawn a caring response from an extraordinarily large number of well-wishers have included births, the occasional illness within the group and, of course, Christmas. During the festive season Jambo, his females and their offspring would find themselves the recipients of yet more cards and also small presents, the latter often being in the form of items of gift-wrapped fruit. Jersey resident Mrs Sylvia Graucob, who, through the Trust's adoption scheme, has for a number of years accepted responsibility for Kishka and her daughter Sakina, still annually ensures that each gorilla has a box of dates or figs as a festive treat. Similarly, Christmas mornings continue to find zoo director, Jeremy Mallinson, distributing liberal helpings of fruit cake and cheese to his gorilla friends, the fruit cake in particular always having been a great favourite of Jambo's.

Adopting an animal at the Trust basically involves paying a yearly subscription which then goes towards the cost of its upkeep. In exchange, the adopter receives a photograph of their chosen specimen along with detailed information about it, and a certificate acknowledging their valuable contribution. The scheme has proved very successful, so much so that the seemingly endless number of adoption plaques to be found around the zoo grounds confused one young visitor into exclaiming to his mother, 'Look there's another one who's been adopted. I wonder why there are so many orphans in this zoo?'

Mrs Catherine Heppe from the USA, who took over Jambo's adoption in 1981, wrote regularly enquiring about him and his growing family, and never let a birthday or Christmas go by without sending a card and donation. She also crossed the Atlantic several times to visit the Trust where, needless to say, she spent the majority of her time at the gorilla complex watching 'My beloved Jambo'.

Shortly after Christmas, while Asato commenced cutting his first teeth, his upper incisors, and continued to endure the smothering attentions of both N'pongo and the irrepressible Hlala Kahilli, another Jersey-born gorilla was making zoological history on the other side of the world.

On 30 December, one week after his eighth birthday, Motaba became a father. For his female, thirty-four-year-old Betsy, it was also her first baby and, not surprisingly, she had displayed all the symptoms of an older woman's pregnancy – a desultory labour which, after some twenty-two hours, had required medical intervention in the form of a Caesarean section to deliver a 2.4 kg male, who was eventually named Buzandi, 'preciousness' in the dialect spoken by the Ila people of Zimbabwe.

Buzundi's birth was a thoroughly deserved success for a zoo that had spared no expense in providing an excellent and very naturalistic environment for its gorillas. As the director, Professor Graham Mitchell, emphasized in a letter of thanks to the Trust, it was considered an event of great zoological importance:

Dear JWPT,
Thanks for your congratulations and best wishes on the arrival of Jambo's grandson. We regard this birth to be significant for several reasons:

a) It's only the second gorilla to be born in Australia;

b) It's the first naturally conceived gorilla to be born in Australia (the male Mzuri, or Ya Kwanza, having been born through artificial insemination in 1984);

c) It's possibly only the third gorilla to be delivered by Caesarean section;

d) Betsy is possibly the oldest first-time mother.

After many years of trying to breed gorillas, our major breakthrough came when the JWPT offered to send young Jersey-born Motaba. After a brief settling in period, Motaba mated with both our females. We hope he will follow in his father's footsteps, and that this will be the first of many of Jambo's grandchildren to be born in Australia.

It was very welcome news with which to end 1991, and equally gratifying to be able to announce to Trust members that Jambo's fifteenth grandoffspring had arrived.

KISHKA'S
ASSISTED DELIVERY

The early part of 1992 saw Asato making excellent progress in spite of the fact that in February his mother experienced a temporary lactation problem when, due to a suspected abscess, milk flow was interrupted on her left side, causing the breast to become greatly enlarged. Dr Simon Slaffer duly put N'pongo on a course of Flucloxacillin, an antibiotic which, in time, reduced her painfully swollen mammary to about a 40D cup size. Prior to making a full recovery, the elderly female's uncomfortable lop-sided appearance drew outpourings of heart-felt sympathy from many human mothers: 'Oh poor thing, I know just how she feels.'

Kishka, meanwhile, was in the final stages of her second pregnancy and looked to be the picture of health – albeit a very large picture. Since the late 1970s, gorilla births at the Trust had conveniently occurred at fairly close intervals, which meant that the group's mother-reared offspring had each been able to benefit from the all-important companionship provided by either a half or full sibling during their formative years: N'gola and Kakinga; Motaba and Rafiki; Sakina and Hlala Kahilla. With Asato still less than six months of age, it was assumed that, all being well, Kishka's baby would eventually continue this very successful pattern.

The expectant mother carefully chose her time to go into labour. No sooner had Dr Slaffer left after an early Saturday morning visit to check on N'pongo's breast condition than Kishka suddenly began passing fluids and quantities of blood. Then, squatting in various positions around the left-hand enclosure, she calmly commenced touching herself, wiping her vulva with woodwool and sniffing and licking her fingers. I immediately alerted other staff members, grabbed the video camera and a notebook and, trying desperately to overcome the butterflies in my stomach, began recording my observations. I could clearly feel my heart thumping in anticipation as I attempted to focus the camera on Kishka's rear end. My hands were shaking and I had to take several deep breaths in order to steady myself. Kishka, in total contrast, appeared to be quite relaxed and in control. She continued gingerly to examine herself in between contractions, and even allowed Sakina and Hlala Kahilli the privilege of doing the same.

Having instinctively sensed what was about to happen, the two youngsters had quickly approached to investigate, and now they closely followed Kishka's every move. N'pongo, on the other hand, was simply content to nurse her son and watch from a distance – for her it was just all too familiar. Whilst G-Ann and Julia, having already galloped off outside, remained playfully oblivious to all that was going on, Jambo and Nandi, who still occupied the right-hand area, decided to take advantage of a grandstand view of the proceedings. Both grumbled loudly when Kishka moved towards the partition and even Nandi seemed content to overlook the rivalry that had long existed between herself and her silverback's second-favourite female.

During the following twenty-five minutes, Kishka experienced five more contractions, each of which she accompanied with a squat and a further discharge of blood. Then a small, pale-coloured protuberance was identified as being part of the umbilical cord. Within a minute, she had extended this to a clearly visible loop of around 100 mm (4 in), by carefully using handfuls of woodwool to grip and pull on the slippery tube – behaviour interpreted at the same time by mammal curator, Bryan Carroll, as being 'tool use in adversity'.

Kishka's attention now became focused entirely on the cord. She began pulling on it harder and harder and, as she did so, the first signs of agitation appeared. Her stools loosened, and she became suddenly irritated by the close proximity of Sakina who, because of her mother's condition, proved extremely difficult to discourage. Within half an hour, the loop of umbilical cord was close to 50 cm (20 in) in length and, as I recorded Kishka's increasing physical discomfort, thoughts came to mind of an almost identical situation which had involved her mother Shamba some fifteen years earlier. Back in June 1977, I had seen Howletts' most senior female exhibit much the same behaviour when trying to give birth to what turned out to be a breech-positioned baby. Shamba had created such tremendous tension pulling on the umbilical cord that it had broken, severing the lifeline of the baby, who was stillborn ten minutes later.

Kishka, however, continued making a determined effort. Grunting and grimacing with pain, she pushed hard with each contraction, then reached down feeling hopefully for signs of her infant, only to find the pinched loop of umbilical cord. Several times, she bent over forwards, straining desperately in an attempt to see for herself just what was happening. The answer remained the same – very little. I had serious doubts that she would be able to deliver the baby herself, and decided to move the remainder of the group outside, with the exception of Sakina, so that in the event of having to intervene, there would be maximum room for manoeuvre. Surprisingly, they were all fairly cooperative, though I did have to trick Jambo into thinking that he was to be allowed back into Kishka's area, by opening her access door an inch or two.

Once Jambo's area had been cleaned, Kishka and her daughter were coaxed across into more comfortable surroundings, and the situation was reviewed. As a precaution, the zoo's vets had informed their colleagues at the General Hospital of Kishka's predicament and had immediately received a voluntary offer to stand by ready to assist. Then, shortly before 11.00 am one of the island's top gynaecologists, Mr John Day, called in to see if he could help. In his considered opinion, Kishka was experiencing an obstructed labour, which really warranted an EUA, or extraction under anaesthetic.

The hospital team was contacted, and preparations were made ready across at the veterinary centre to receive the patient.

Within the hour, Kishka had been isolated and anaesthetized by dart. She succumbed quickly, and I entered the area to retrieve the syringe and check on her breathing. A few minutes later, I was joined by John Day who, after making a close inspection, began to manipulate the cord and what soon proved to be the baby's right foot.

Then, very gradually and with considerable effort, he expertly eased out the lifeless form of a full-term male infant. 'What a shame . . . lovely baby,' he remarked, and patted the slumbering Kishka on the rump. Indeed it was a great shame, but at least Kishka, unlike her mother, had been spared the sight of her dead offspring.

On completion of a thorough examination, the hefty female was transferred by stretcher to one of the smaller and more secluded back dens where, thankfully, she very soon began to regain consciousness. There, reclining on a deep litter of woodwool, she was able to recuperate.

By 3.00 pm Kishka was sitting up and taking drinks. Still a little unsteady, she occasionally held on to me for support and, at times, allowed her massive head to loll sideways to rest on my shoulder. Her breathing, though heavy, was regular and hot on my neck. It had been a traumatic experience for her, but despite all the discomfort and human interference, she remains a very stable and trusting individual who, like her resilient mother, will no doubt go on to produce further healthy offspring – following her own stillbirth, Shamba's next infant had, in fact, been the beautiful Kishka.

NANDI AND JAMBO

Certain gorilla emotions are clearly discernable. For several weeks after losing her baby, Kishka suffered post-natal depression, often lying motionless in her day nest for long periods, either sleeping or simply staring vacantly about. When feeling up to it, she would join the group outside for an occasional constitutional, though mostly she chose to keep a low profile and tolerated only the close proximity of Sakina and Hlala Kahilli. Nevertheless, by the end of the month, she was beginning once again to function in a manner befitting her social position.

The competitive nature of the gorilla can be seen in the behaviour of even the youngest group member. Already recognizable in the rough-and-tumble antics of the infant, it becomes increasingly more evident throughout the juvenile and sub-adult stages, before finally culminating in the struggle for status amongst the adults.

Kishka, though long since accepted as top female by the others of Jambo's harem, still found herself having to contend with the odd aggressive encounter. She also had to deal with the occasional spontaneous outburst from Nandi, which seemed to be motivated more by jealousy over the silverback than by contention of rank. Confrontations of this nature usually erupted when the older female attempted to oust the stolid Kishka from the vicinity of their patriarch. Her patience quickly exhausted, Nandi would precipitate conflict by advancing in a menacing strut with hair bristling, at the same time throwing quite evil sidelong glances at her adversary. Then, coughing angrily, she would tentatively reach out towards a tight-lipped Kishka, testing for an opening, for a chance to lunge forward to grab and so unbalance her rival. In acceptance of the challenge, Kishka would seek to do the same. Sparring like this sometimes occupied several minutes with both contestants' mouths agape and their cough grunts giving way to short penetrating barks that, in turn, would swell into full-blooded screams.

Jambo seemed reluctant to intervene and often could be seen foraging in fairly relaxed fashion only a short distance away as his two prized females, stimulated by a mutual abrasive quality, battled furiously. Only in the event of others joining in would he assert his authority. Usually this involved him ploughing directly into their squabbling midst, a well-practised and controlled manoeuvre that always had the desired effect.

Although she had to concede a distinct size and weight advantage to the younger female, the fiercely determined Nandi was usually the one responsible for prolonging their encounters. Often, by the time a stalemate or stand-off situation had been reached, both main participants would be showing clear signs of fatigue, resting heavily on their knuckles and blowing hard.

Then, on the morning of 3 April 1992, I entered the gorilla house to discover Nandi stretched out as if sleeping, although she was on the floor instead of lying in one of her more favoured nesting sites up on a raised level or on the suspended platform. The portly little thirty-four-year-old had passed away in the presence of her trusted and much-adored companion, Jambo. Clearly upset, the powerful male was extremely reluctant to leave her side, and displayed the same degree of concern for her as he had done back in May 1989, at the time of her Caesarean section.

Now, once again, he paced anxiously, barely audible hoot vocalizations denoting his mood. As I approached, he confronted me at the window, standing upright with his massive hands flat on the glass. He stared directly into my face. Then, retaining this stance, he kept abreast of me along the glass barrier of the exhibition area, and was waiting at the barred door when I entered the service porch. He stopped vocalizing, but continued to look searchingly at me as I tried to reassure him, though I was equally shocked and upset. Poor Nandi was lying on her back, directly behind him and, as I bent to make a close inspection, Jambo instantly dropped down on to all fours to block my view. Perhaps suspicious of what I might do, he maintained this position throughout my observations and, no matter which way I turned, kept his huge frame protectively between me and his female.

The other females and offspring in the adjacent area, alert to Jambo's anguished state, were noticeably unsettled and equally curious about the strangely inert form of one of their most influential group members. It was clearly an upsetting experience for all, and so I hastened to get them outside as quickly as possible. I was then faced with the problem of what to do with Jambo. Hooting quietly to himself, he paced restlessly back and forth. He had already refused to leave the building and showed no inclination to cross over into the left-hand exhibition area. Instead, whenever I opened a slide, he would return to sit directly next to Nandi, sometimes resting a hand upon her, while staring accusingly across at me. He obviously knew exactly what I intended.

Eventually, after much talking and numerous changes of tactics, I finally persuaded him to leave her. He still wouldn't go outside, but did compromise and allow himself to be enticed into the adjoining enclosure, where he quickly displayed his highly charged emotional state with several strutting runs and repeated hammerings on the partition. Due to his stubbornness, I found myself with no other choice than to remove the distressing figure of Nandi while he looked on. I tried to do this as quickly as I could, but during my struggle to ease her on to a trolley, he suddenly let out a harsh, barking scream, expressing his anguish and anger. The heart-breaking sound went right through me. Then, seconds later, she was gone, out of his sight for ever.

Nandi had died without warning, with no visible signs of illness or discomfort. Her post-mortem examination, however, revealed an obstruction in the large intestine, with death being attributed to aspiration pneumonia. In addition, a histological examination exposed a cardiomyopathy (underlying heart disease).

Jambo continued to be greatly affected by Nandi's death, and mourned her passing for several weeks. To a degree, he became unsociable and, at times, seemed all too easily irritated both by members of his group and myself. When alone, he tended to lose his appetite, often refusing all forms of sustenance outright with a bad-tempered slam of a mighty forearm against the barred door. It was terribly sad to see him sitting so sullen faced and depressed, knowing that, only time, if anything, could heal the emotional pain of his loss.

END OF AN ERA

Throughout most of his twenty years at the Trust, Jambo enjoyed excellent health. Illnesses, fortunately, had been few and rarely serious enough to affect his voracious appetite. So when he failed to appear for his midday feed on Thursday 10 September 1992, I became immediately curious.

As it was a pleasantly warm and sunny day, at first I imagined him to be slumbering on his irregular-shaped elm-board bench at the far end of the enclosure. Instead, on rounding a corner, I discovered him sitting quietly, hands resting across his knees, watching my approach. I called out to him several times, and gestured with his feed bucket, tapping it against the wall, a familiar sound that he and his group associated with food. Still he failed to respond. His expression never changed and he made no move, though he did manage one of his deep resonant belly grumbles when, moments later, I dropped a slice of brown wholemeal bread down on to the grass close to him. However, even this was not enough to tempt him, and the prize was quickly claimed by the impish Hlala Kahilli, who proceeded to demolish it noisily, whilst squatting directly in front of her father.

After feeding the other members of the group, I returned to check on Jambo. He was in a similar position, resting with his back against the perimeter wall, only now his eyes were closed against the brightness of the midday sun. Above him, a party of French visitors were doing their best to attract his attention but, despite their pleas, he remained motionless.

By late afternoon, Jambo had moved to a spot some twenty metres along the base of the wall which, being practically the sum total of his day's activity, presented further cause for concern. Shortly before 5.00 pm the females began to amble towards the house in readiness for their last meal of the day, but even their high-pitched choruses of expectant whines and grumbles failed to arouse the silverback who paid them little heed as they filed off past him and into their quarters. This was most unlike him – Jams was definitely feeling unwell.

I had informed the zoo's veterinary staff of Jambo's earlier behaviour and, having anticipated a possible reluctance on his part to come inside for the night, had also requested their presence at the complex to help entice him in. Unfortunately for vets, it is often the case that their patients will associate them with the discomfort of illness, and subsequent unpleasant treatments or injections. When dealing with an intelligent, sensitive individual such as the gorilla, the vet can at best expect to be received with a degree of suspicion and, sometimes, outright aggression. Jambo decided on the latter.

Picking out consultant vet, Nick Blampied, from the group assembled at the wall close to the gorilla building, he slowly eased himself up into a sitting position. Then, realizing just who he was focusing on, he quickly rose to all fours and tensed visibly, the hairs on his neck and shoulders becoming erect. Although I knew more or less what was to follow, and tried to steady myself in readiness, Jambo's opening barrage of alarm barks still made me jump. Before their echoes had subsided he broke into a stiff-legged, strutting trot. Checking momentarily, he refocused and then gathered himself before launching into a full-blooded roaring charge up towards our highly embarrassed voluntary bait.

Once Nick had moved into the internal public viewing area, I quickly operated the door to admit the angry patient. Without hesitation, he burst through the curtain of plastic draught excluders and threw himself at the window of toughened glass with a tremendous thump, forcing those nearby to take several involuntary steps backwards. 'If he's sick, I wouldn't like to see what he is capable of when he's well,' said a shaky voice. Having served his immediate purpose, Nick Blampied, smiling sheepishly, quietly slipped outside.

Despite this brief, though impressive, display Jambo was clearly off-colour. Once settled he showed a worrying early reluctance to take liquids and, although later that evening he consumed most of his fruit feed, it wasn't without some coaxing.

Over the next few days Jambo, though always eager to be with his group, began gradually to limit his own physical contact with them. Whereas normally he would intervene to settle minor disputes over forage or to minimize teasing or bullying amongst the younger members, he became slow to do so, and occasionally squabbles escalated to more serious proportions. Julia and G-Ann suddenly seemed less intimidated by him, and could often be seen appearing quite relaxed and confident in his immediate proximity. His younger offspring, as usual, continued to seek his company but, fond of them as he was, even here the ailing patriarch kept his own exertions to a minimum by simply allowing them to clamber over him, to grab and play-bite at his hands and feet, or to tug and twist the long thick black shiny twirls of hair that covered his massive shoulders and arms.

Meanwhile, veterinary investigations had begun. Samples of Jambo's urine were found to contain traces of blood, and subsequently a course of Amoxycillin was recommended on a tentative diagnosis of a urino-genital infection.

By 14 September Jambo seemed brighter. He was more enthusiastic about his food, picking out favoured items from his midday vegetable feed, and his liquid intake was also increasing. His medication was being accepted without fuss, and he showed no further desire to be left outside on his own after 5.30 pm. His activity level was still below par, but I was beginning to feel a little happier about his condition and, that evening, I recorded his much-improved behaviour on video tape.

Over the years I must have shot hours and hours of film of Jambo and his group during introductions, play, matings, births, rearing and, occasionally, when they have been ill. The footage of his bold display some days earlier was in total contrast to the lethargy that had followed; but in equal contrast to such sad pictures are the last pieces of film that I took of him as he fed that evening, grumbling as he often did with sheer enjoyment.

Throughout the following day, Jambo maintained his improved form, and came indoors with his group a little earlier than usual, the weather being considerably cooler. He cleared his entire late-afternoon meal and, when I looked in on him before leaving, he was deftly nipping the leaves from some willow stems with mobile lips, quickly drawing them into his mouth and then chewing on them contentedly. He glanced across at me when I said 'Goodnight' and grumbled in reply, then resumed foraging.

Shortly before 8 am on Wednesday 16 September I turned on the lights in the exhibition hall and found Jambo lying very still, close to the central barred partition. For a few heart-stopping seconds I stared in disbelief, not wanting to accept what my uncomfortable gut feeling told me. Hoping desperately that I was wrong, I hurriedly unlocked the door to his area and entered. I crossed over to where he lay, grabbed his left forearm and began shaking it while repeating his name over and over ridiculously loudly. His arm, though incredibly heavy, moved easily from the elbow and he was warm to the touch. He lay on his back, though his head and the top half of his body were inclined slightly to the right, and his left arm extended across his chest and on to the floor. It appeared as if, earlier that morning, Jambo had been sitting at the partition, probably either interacting with his offspring or simply watching them. The toes of his left foot still protruded through the mesh and, even as I tried to take in the immensity of what had happened, I noticed eleven-month-old Asato gripping and play-biting them, seemingly unaware of his father's demise.

The females, N'pongo, Kishka, Sakina and Hlala Kahilli crowded

142

the partition. All remained silent apart from N'pongo who, irritated by my clumsy and rather futile attempts to revive her mate, cough-grunted with annoyance. However, her threats quickly faded, and I laid Jambo's arm gently down on to his chest. His family were clearly nervous and as upset as I was. We were all confused and totally devastated. I stroked his incredible head – his features were quite relaxed and, even in death, he look magnificent. He retained all his dignity, and for the very last time, I felt humble in his presence and, I am not ashamed to say, very emotional.

The following week, a memorandum to the JWPT's Board of Management from Tony Allchurch, zoo veterinarian, read:

The adult male lowland gorilla, Jambo, was found dead on the morning of Wednesday 16th September, 1992, by his keeper, Richard Johnstone-Scott.

Although he had been receiving attention in the preceding week, his death was quite sudden and unexpected.

Post-mortem examination was carried out the same afternoon at the Pathology Department of the General Hospital, under the direction of David Spencer, the Consultant Pathologist, assisted by Peter Corcoran, Senior Pathology Technician.

Cause of death was easily determined, and was due to spontaneous rupture of the major artery, resulting in a massive haemorrhage in the chest. The cause of this catastrophic event was a dissecting aneurysm of the ascending and descending sections of the aorta.

Dissecting aneurysm most commonly occurs in the forty to sixty year age group in man, and is two or three times more frequent in the male than female. Hypertension is almost invariably an antecedent (94% of cases) of the condition. Death occurs within fifteen minutes of onset of symptoms in 25% of cases and, of those who survive, a further 75% die within one week.

Diagnosis and treatment are very difficult and although progress is being made in surgical techniques, prognosis is very poor in 95% of cases.

In other words, there was nothing that anyone could have done to prevent Jambo's death. Knowing this did little to ease the terrible sadness felt by all of those who had cared for him, and perhaps by the non-human primates who had been cared for by him. And he would be mourned far beyond the boundaries of the Jersey Zoo.

News of Jambo's passing travelled quickly and every employee at the Trust was visibly shaken, some being reduced to tears. The local media, which in the past had publicized numerous happier events connected with the island's most popular resident and his seemingly ever-increasing family, paid a number of fitting tributes to him in the form of articles, announcements and a TV profile, which included a rescreening of the internationally acclaimed CTV documentary programme *Jambo – The Gentle Giant*. Cards and letters of condolence began to arrive in large numbers, as further proof of the high esteem in which so many people had held him.

While it is often considered unscientific and sentimental to refer to animals in human terms, I subscribe to the theory that to think along anthropomorphic lines can, in fact, serve to enhance our understanding of animal behaviour, and put it in a more meaningful context, particularly when the individuals concerned happen to be of the highest order of primate. To most people, Jambo will always be remembered as the big gorilla who saved the little boy, though I hope that this biography, with its many lapses into anthropomorphism, will have shown him to be much more than simply an amiable ape. There is, however, no doubt that his quite natural reaction towards the stricken child helped immeasurably to restore in the public mind the good nature and character of such a noble anthropoid as the gorilla.

In recognition of that simple deed, and as a tribute to Jambo, the

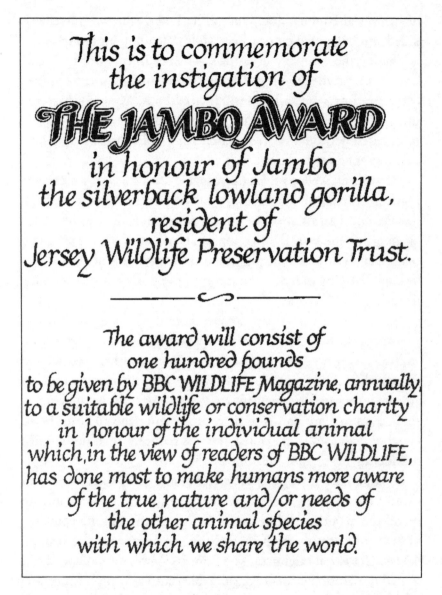

This is to commemorate
the instigation of

THE JAMBO AWARD

in honour of Jambo
the silverback lowland gorilla,
resident of
Jersey Wildlife Preservation Trust.

⎯⎯⎯⎯ ⌒〜 ⎯⎯⎯⎯

The award will consist of
one hundred pounds
to be given by BBC WILDLIFE Magazine, annually,
to a suitable wildlife or conservation charity
in honour of the individual animal
which, in the view of readers of BBC WILDLIFE,
has done most to make humans more aware
of the true nature and/or needs of
the other animal species
with which we share the world.

BBC's *Wildlife Magazine* announced shortly after the incident the creation of a new award in Jambo's honour. Appropriately, the first £100 from the BBC was awarded to the Digit Fund (now the Dian Fossey Gorilla Fund), established by the late Dian Fossey in memory of her world-famous mountain gorilla Digit, who was mercilessly killed and butchered by poachers while defending his group.

Sharing the company of gorillas, whether in the wild or in captivity, is a privilege enjoyed by very few and I consider myself extremely fortunate to have experienced both. My work has, over the years, provided me with the opportunity to observe and, in most cases, get to know many fascinating individuals – yet Jambo will always be very special.

He was a marvellous character, capable of a variety of guises ranging from the dominant, strutting silverback, impressing both his females and visitors alike, to the big softy enjoying a game with a gushing hosepipe in the privacy of an off-show area. Here, in a relaxed mood, he would play, vigorously washing his hands and feet, and soaking everything in sight in the process, while burbling like an excited juvenile.

Like many of his species, he greatly enjoyed being tickled and would eagerly offer himself at the partition, often gurgling uncontrollably, with his cavernous jaws wide open and his eyes screwed tightly shut in anticipation. If tricked into having his armpits attacked, he would immediately slam his huge biceps tight to his side, trapping my hands and so prolonging the tickling bout. Giggling hysterically, he would then be reduced to an undignified shuddering heap, until breathless.

Looking back it seems appropriate that Jambo's last few months should have spanned the warmth of summer, enabling him to spend the majority of those precious days in the adoring company of his family. It was also perhaps fitting that earlier in the year, on 4 May, Her Royal Highness, The Princess Royal, should have again visited the Trust and spent considerable time enjoying the spectacle of the silverback and his group, remarking: 'A splendid sight, and they look so content.'

AFTERMATH

Throughout the weeks that followed the death of their patriarch, Jersey's leaderless group experienced a partial breakdown in its social structure. Perhaps most noticeable were the suddenly all too frequent bouts of unruly behaviour indulged in by the younger females, often instigated by the unpredictable G-Ann. She and Sakina were both initially responsible for teasing and harassing N'pongo and her offspring, with Asato in particular being the main focus of their attention. To his obvious dismay, he found himself regularly kidnapped, sometimes even being cheekily snatched from his jockey-seat high up on N'pongo's greying shoulders, and though no real harm befell him, his shrill cries of protest would echo around the enclosure, until his ageing mother was able to catch up and intervene.

Mostly, Asato was subjected only to the kind of treatment that his peers and older siblings had themselves gone through during their formative years. The teasing or bullying of immatures, or of those less confident, by juveniles and sub-adults is not uncommon in gorilla society. For the young, it is all part of their growing up and establishing a position for themselves in the extended family. Sadly, though, sessions of this nature tended to become increasingly prolonged and when, a short time later, Hlala Kahilli added to the situation by also mischievously bullying her younger brother, family relationships were tested to the full. One incident involving N'pongo and her bickering offspring even ended up with the beleaguered mother requiring minor surgery to a small superficial artery in her leg that had been severed by a bad-tempered nip.

After Jambo's death, Julia too suddenly found herself having to fend off some obnoxious behaviour from G-Ann, and contend with the more serious threats of redirected aggression from

147

a frustrated and highly agitated N'pongo. It seemed rather unfair that the younger female, having so recently weathered many a scuffle during the demanding period of her integration, should once again become the recipient of a number of clearly unwarranted attacks.

With Jambo gone it fell to the steady, composed and benevolent Kishka gradually, through sheer force of character, to bring about some semblance of order and thus end the social discord that had developed within the group. Though the largest and most powerful animal, with readily apparent leadership qualities, she rarely chose to exercise her physical superiority, relying instead on the psychological approach. Her strutting presence and testing, intermittent bouts of unwavering eye contact more often than not proved effective in de-fusing tense situations. Unfortunately, while Sakina and Hlala Kahilli were quick to heed such warning signals, the rebellious G-Ann was not, and a number of aggressive confrontations took place.

Though separated only by a seven-month age gap, Kishka was by far the more mature of the two and would exhibit a confident and silent approach, while her volatile opponent emitted a continual flow of staccato cough grunts and barks. However, despite the competition being fast and furious, injuries sustained amounted usually to little more than minor lacerations. It was as if these two females of contrasting personalities, having both come a long way since their respective transfers into the Jersey group, knew well enough one another's physical capabilities, and so were content simply to release a bit of tension.

The spring of 1993 saw a marked improvement in the compatibility of Kiskha's group. Normality, albeit in the absence of a dominant male, returned to the colony. Overall, Kishka remains comfortably in position as number one female, while Spider, it seems, is on equal footing for second place with the ever-mellowing N'pongo. Julia now appears to occupy the next hierarchial slot, with Sakina and Hlala Kahilli being too preoccupied with having fun to concern themselves, at this stage in their lives, with serious orders of rank.

Despite maintaining her predominantly lively and playful ways, Hlala Kahilli, shortly after the death of her father, did develop a nervous habit of clasping her hands up around the sides of her head whenever unsure of herself or of a situation. For some time, this stress-related behaviour persisted and often preceded particularly vigorous bullying sessions involving Asato, which subsequently required all the more rapid intervention by N'pongo. It is, perhaps, a measure of the young female's deeply felt loss that it was not until some eight months later that I noticed a marked decrease in her displays.

Working as I do on a daily basis with the group, it is sometimes difficult to appreciate just how quickly youngsters do mature and grow up. Many a time I have found myself suddenly realizing that little 'whoever' is now old enough to reproduce. And often it is not until a new infant is born that the growth and development of others is put into some sort of visual perspective.

The fact that Sakina is now a sexually mature female has, perhaps, been somewhat masked by her outgoing and generally mischievous nature. Even during oestrus, her ridiculously exaggerated behaviour tends to be more play-oriented than sexual. The clown-like balancing of small grass turves or pieces of bark upon her neck, as if trying to improve her deportment, or the carrying of twigs, clamped firmly in her mouth, all form part of an extensive repertoire denoting her receptivity. Though bordering on the absurd, these and other similar antics did not dissuade her father from vocally acknowledging her monthly condition throughout the latter part of his last summer – an indication that she would shortly have to be transferred to another collection. Now, however, both Sakina and Hlala Kahilli will remain in the Jersey group of the future, for which a young, though sexually mature and genetically valuable, male has been selected.

It is to be Melbourne Zoo's nine-year-old Ya Kwanza, popularly called Mzuri. He is of wild-caught parentage, though he was actually conceived through artificial insemination. It is hoped that, like his predecessor, he will in time earn the respect and trust of the Jersey group, and over the forthcoming twenty years prove himself to be as productive. Clearly he has a lot to live up to.

While the Melbourne male is experienced with companions of his own age and upwards, he has barely had any exposure to younger individuals. Consequently, his reactions toward the likes of Hlala Kahilli and Asato will be carefully monitored, though by all accounts he is a good-natured animal who should eventually prove acceptable – even, it is hoped, to the extrovert G-Ann.

Now fourteen, G-Ann has developed into an extraordinary character who demands attention and who usually gets it. Her moods are many and can be influenced as much by humans as by those of her own species. She is initially suspicious of most people, and is easily disturbed by the sight of an unfamiliar face behind the scenes, such as in the kitchen or service areas of the building. When surprised in this way, she displays accordingly, and at times will redirect her feelings of agitation towards any subordinate group member who happens to be within reach. On one such occasion, when upset by the presence of a new keeper, she chose me and promptly inflicted a deep bite to my right forearm as I rather foolishly tried to reassure her at the wrong moment. Excruciatingly painful as it was, I like to think that my being subjected to such behaviour was an indication of total acceptance, and that perhaps in Spider's mind I am considered to be as much an important part of her life as any other group member.

Meanwhile with Kishka, nothing has changed. Her promotion seems to have made no difference at all to our working relationship, and she remains as stable and cooperative as ever. She has even adopted one of Jambo's particularly useful habits, and now regularly takes it upon herself to ensure that the plastic draught excluder flaps are clear of the runners each evening, so that the doors can be closed without delay. Assuming the responsibilities of group leader has not altered her basically gentle disposition, and she continues to earn the respect of her female companions, while retaining the affections of the youngsters.

Despite the not infrequent rough-house attentions of Hlala Kahilli, which often appear to be motivated by jealousy, Asato can still be found spending lengthy periods in her company. Together with Julia and Sakina, they form an actively entertaining little band, and have seemingly endless reserves of energy for playing tag or sparring.

Although many observers are able to relate quite easily to these behaviours, few can individually identify the participants. Jambo was an obvious and unmistakable figure: his females and progeny remain far less distinguishable from one another. 'How on earth do you tell them apart?' is a familiar question. But close study reveals that each varies conspicuously in their physical and behavioural traits, while another source of identification, adopted in early field studies, relies upon 'nose prints' – As no two humans have exactly the same finger-prints, no two gorillas have the same shape of nostrils, around which are intricate patterns of troughs and ridges.

Now thirty-five years old, N'pongo continues to look fit and well and, though her coat has paled with age, it retains a healthy sheen. Many years of rearing offspring seem to have had little effect on her general condition, though her suckling of Asato currently gives her the all too conspicuous build of a nursing female, making her easier to identify. Facially, she has not really changed that much since her youth, but her intimidating looks can be misleading. A fixed sombre expression now for the most part masks a gentler dis-position, which eventually brought even this wily old girl to a state of near-reconciliation with Jambo. N'pongo's strong, serious fea-tures are easily recognizable in her offspring. The firm set, pro-truding jaw and flattened nose are overhung by heavily prominent brow ridges, directly beneath which are set very brooding brown eyes that are one of her most striking characteristics.

While Hlala Kahilli's countenance already closely resembles that of her mother, Asato has yet to lose his looks of wide-eyed innocence. Food and play are his priorities, and the latter he will happily indulge in whether accompanied or alone. Carefree, he can be seen scampering about, sporting a conspicuous white anal patch, not dissimilar to a rabbit's bob, which will remain visible throughout his infancy and into early juvenescence. The actual significance of this marking in young gorillas has never really been explained, but possibly it may serve to assist adult females in maintaining visual contact with their offspring in the subdued light of the forest – or it may simply denote age-group status of the latter to other family members.

Usually not far away from his captivating performances can be found the lanky Sakina. At seven years of age, she is at that difficult stage of early sub-adulthood, a period when sometimes play activities can be interrupted by budding maternal instincts or sexual awareness. Round-headed and long-limbed, she moves at times with a relaxed gangling step which is unmistakable, even from a distance. When running she, like the other younger animals, progresses slightly sideways with one shoulder lifted in front of the other, ready to barge aside any obstruction.

Though gorillas are primarily quadrupedal, the upright stance is frequently adopted, and of the Jersey group Julia, in particular, favours prolonged two-legged locomotion. Propelled by a comical waddle and paddling arms, her ability to regularly cover distances exceeding twenty metres or more makes this very much a Julia trait. Back on all fours, her locomotion is not unlike that of the short-stepped steady plod of N'pongo, which is contrastingly different to both Kishka's supple rolling gate and the almost purposeful military strut of G-Ann.

G-Ann, like N'pongo, has the classic, conical head shape, though perhaps a little more exaggerated in places. Over recent years, her crest has become increasingly pronounced and reminds me of a scaled-down version of a Red Indian. war bonnet, which trembles whenever she is on the move.

The coats of most of the group are predominantly dark, mainly charcoal coloured, shot through in places with lighter flecks of grey. Added to this, and highlighted especially by the brightness of summer, are subtle shades of brown, visible on the upper arms, shoulders and back, while a more vivid splash adorns the top of the head and disappears into the crest.

Jambo's physique and colouring had been even more spectacular. His splendid profile was crowned with a marvellous sagittal crest, a feature especially prominent in adult males, and one which provides an attachment for the large temporal muscles that operate their powerful jaws. Spreading upwards from his forehead, the short, even hair was of that familiar deep russet hue, while a salt-and-pepper flecking cascaded down the back and sides of a huge neck to spread out and darken over his massive shoulders; longer, shaggier, pale charcoal-coloured tufts grew down and round from the bulging supra-orbital ridge that overhung the eyes, framing and enhancing a stern, yet very handsome and intelligent face.

His shoulders and arms were simply magnificent. Of enormous proportions, they were heavily draped in thick, jet-black sleeves of long glossy whorls which formed a quite startling contrast to the short, silvery-white hair of clipped appearance that covered his broad saddle, lower back and muscular rump; a 'silverback' of exceptional quality, who will always be remembered with very great affection.

For visitors new to the Trust, Jambo appears now only as one of many portraits on the gorilla family-tree board. Positioned as he is, directly beneath his parents and in the midst of the females, his noble features are the focal point of a display that is both an illustration of his breeding prowess, and a photographic record of the progeny who themselves as individuals over the years had considerable bearing on the gradual change in composition of the Jersey group. To date, ten of their number currently reside in separate collections in six different countries. In all Jambo sired fifteen live offspring (including Tam Tam at Basle Zoo) from nineteen pregnancies, and with the majority of these having themselves reproduced Jambo, at the time of his passing, had fifteen living grand-offspring, from a total of twenty-three births to his credit . . . and still they continue to arrive.

It is perhaps typical of the way the media work that the 'Jambo and the boy' incident should have enjoyed a sort of renaissance of interest in the last two years, with documentary and drama-documentary programmes being produced by major television companies in the United Kingdom, Europe and in the United States. Whether newsreel footage, reconstructions using actors or new interviews with those involved, all received primetime viewing spots and were watched by millions, confirming that what took place at the Trust on that sunny afternoon back in 1986 was not just a one-day wonder. Instead, it came across as such a powerful image and story that it will surely endure for all time, and with it the memory of a very special non-human primate.

For those who knew him, Jambo was the embodiment of the strong, wise and protective patriarch, whose offspring tumbled and wrestled about him, secure in the knowledge that he was there. His females, both young and mature, clearly respected him, though he had his preferences and some would always enjoy a closer relationship with him than others. Yet from beneath a heavy brow, he surveyed them all as his, with a searching gaze that could either reassure or intimidate. Powerful in stature, yet capable of great gentleness, his very presence was itself a major contribution to his species.

Taking care of Jambo was, for me, a great privilege and one that I enjoyed immensely. Such was his personality that even today he remains conspicuous by his absence . . . he truly was a remarkable gorilla.

Postscript

At approximately 12.30pm on Friday 18 June 1993, a very relaxed Ya Kwanza, or Mzuri, accompanied with his keeper, Ulli Weiher, arrived at the Jersey Wildlife Preservation Trust. Being Australia's first-born gorilla, Ya Kwanza's move was given maximum media coverage. A camera crew even travelled with him to ensure that nothing was missed.

Like his famous predecessor, from day one 'Yukky' has enjoyed celebrity status. Understandably his adoring Australian public hadn't wanted to lose him and demand to be kept informed of his progress. So for Ya Kwanza and the Jersey gorillas, a new era begins . . .

CHRONOLOGICAL HISTORY OF JAMBO'S EXTENDED FAMILY

1957 N'pongo born in the wild, Cameroons
1959 22 November: N'pongo arrived in Jersey
      Nandi born in the wild, Cameroons
1961 17 April: Jambo born in Basle Zoo, Switzerland
      4 November: Nandi arrived in Jersey
1971 2 May: Jambo sires male infant Tam Tam at Basle
      Zoo, Switzerland
      N'pongo and Nandi moved to Brian Park Gorilla Complex
1972 27 April: Jambo arrives in Jersey
      30 April: Brian Park Complex officially opened by
      David Niven
      Jambo introduced to N'pongo and Nandi
1973 15 July: First gorilla birth at JWPT Assumbo, a male infant
      born to Nandi
      11 October: Second gorilla birth at JWPT – Mamfe, a
      male infant born to N'pongo
1974 20 October: Third gorilla birth at JWPT – Zaire, a female
      infant born to Nandi
1975 29 January: Fourth gorilla birth at JWPT – Tatu, a male
      infant born to N'pongo
      31 October: Fifth gorilla birth at JWPT – Bamenda, a female
      infant born to Nandi
1976 11 April: Sixth gorilla birth at JWPT – Kumba, a male
      infant born to N'pongo

23 November: Assumbo and Mamfe sent to Twycross Zoo
on breeding loan

1977   14 January: Seventh gorilla birth at JWPT – a stillborn male
infant born to Nandi

12 April: Salome arrives in Jersey from Zoological Society
of London

21 June: Eighth gorilla birth at JWPT – N'gola, a male infant
born to N'pongo (First mother-reared)

1978   15 March: Kumba sent to Zoological Society of London;
Salome returned to Zoological Society of London

4 October: Work commences on new gorilla complex

1 December: Ninth gorilla birth at JWPT – Kakinga, a male
infant born to Nandi

1979   24 October: First mixings of Nandi and Kakinga with Jambo,
in Brian Park Complex

1980   12 June: N'gola included in mixings

9 December: Zaire, Tatu and Bamenda moved to new
gorilla breeding centre

1981   23 May: Jambo, Nandi and Kakinga moved to new gorilla
breeding centre

30 May: Official opening of gorilla breeding centre by Sir
Peter Whitely

23 June: Tenth gorilla birth at JWPT – Kumi, a female
infant born to N'pongo

10 July: N'pongo, N'gola and Kumi moved to new gorilla
breeding centre

14 July: N'pongo and infants reunited with Nandi and
Kakinga, and introduced to Bamenda

31 July: N'pongo and infants introduced to Zaire, Tatu and
Bamenda

16 August: Zaire escapes from the gorilla breeding centre

6 September: Jambo's father Stephi dies at Basle Zoo,
Switzerland, aged 32

28 November: Kumi dies from injuries received during a fight between Jambo and N'pongo

1982   15 April: Integration of female and offspring group complete (Jambo, Nandi, Kakinga and N'gola forming the alternative permutation)
26 November: Experimental mixing with N'pongo, Nandi and Jambo

1983   8 March: N'pongo's reintroduction to Jambo begins
13 August: Tatu sent to Oklahoma, USA, in exchange
15 August: G-Ann, first unrelated addition to group, arrives in exchange from Oklahoma
23 September: G-Ann's integration begins
23 December: Eleventh gorilla birth at JWPT – Motaba, a male infant born to Nandi

1984   4 March: Twelfth gorilla birth at JWPT – Rafiki, a male infant born to N'pongo
14 April: N'gola sent to Zurich in exchange for Hobbit
7 June: Kumba sent from London Zoo to Chessington Zoo
24 July: Kishka arrives from Howletts
25 July: Zaire sent on breeding loan to Zoological Society of London
25 July: Bamenda sent to Howletts in exchange for Kishka
9 August: Kishka's integration begins
19 August: Hobbit arrives from Zurich
12 September: Hobbit's integration begins
5 October: Visit of HRH The Princess Royal to the gorilla breeding centre
23 November: Kakinga sent to Calgary
12 December: Kishka introduced to Jambo

1985   14 April: Assumbo sent from Twycross Zoo to Chessington Zoo
6 June: Mamfe sired Asante, a female infant, at Twycross Zoo

12 August: Tatu sired Ben, a male infant, at Oklahoma
Zoo, USA

1986   5 May: N'gola sired Moja, a male infant, at Zurich Zoo,
Switzerland
14 July: Thirteenth gorilla birth at JWPT – Sakina, a female
infant born to Kishka
31 August: Levan Meritt falls into gorilla enclosure

1987   3 January: Jambo's mother Achilla dies at Basle Zoo,
Switzerland, aged 39
6 May: G-Ann introduced to Jambo
1 June: Zaire gives birth to Kamili, a female infant, at
London Zoo
22 June: N'gola sires a stillborn male infant at Zurich Zoo,
Switzerland
1 July: N'gola sires Neema, a female infant, at Zurich Zoo,
Switzerland
17 September: N'gola's male infant Moja dies at Zurich Zoo,
Switzerland

1988   23 January: Fourteenth gorilla birth at JWPT – Hlala Kahilli,
a female infant born to N'pongo
20th May: Fifteenth gorilla birth at JWPT – a stillborn male
infant born to Nandi
2 June: Hobbit sent on breeding loan to Pretoria Zoo,
South Africa
9 June: N'gola sires Oya, a female infant, at Zurich Zoo,
Switzerland
26 November: N'gola sires Onji, a female infant, at Zurich
Zoo, Switzerland
2 December: Onji, sired by N'gola, dies at Zurich Zoo,
Switzerland
21 December: Assumbo sent from Chessington Zoo to
Dvur Kralove, Czechoslovakia

1989   27 February: Bamenda gives birth to Kibam, a male infant, at
Howletts Zoo
24 April: Bamenda's male infant Kibam dies at Howletts
2 May: Sixteenth gorilla birth at JWPT – a male infant
delivered dead by Caesarean section to Nandi
17 May: N'gola sires Pendo, a male infant, at Zurich Zoo
6 August: N'gola's infant Pendo dies at Zurich Zoo
28 December: N'gola sires Pole Pole, a male infant, at
Zurich Zoo

1990   10 February: Kumba sires Shani, a female infant, at
Chessington Zoo
16 March: Kumba sires stillborn male infant, at
Chessington Zoo
24 March: Motaba sent on breeding loan to Melbourne
Zoo, Australia
21 May: Julia arrives on deposit from Abuko Nature
Reserve, Gambia
9 September: N'gola sires Quenta, a female infant, at Zurich
Zoo Switzerland
5 September: Assumbo sent from Dvur Kralove to Prague
Zoo, Czechoslovakia
3 December: Julia's integration begins

1991   31 January: Tatu sires a male infant, at Oklahoma Zoo, USA
24 March: Mamfe sires Mambie, a male infant, at Twycross
Zoo
13 May: Tatu's male infant dies at Oklahoma Zoo, USA
29 May: N'gola sires Rafiki, a male infant, at Zurich Zoo,
Switzerland
13 July: Rafiki sent on loan from JWPT – to St Louis Zoo,
USA, to join *first* bachelor group
26 July: Kumba sires Asili, a female infant, at Chessington
Zoo
8 August: N'gola sires Ruya, a female infant, at Zurich Zoo

16 August: Julia introduced to Jambo
20 October: Seventeenth gorilla birth at JWPT – Asato, a male infant born to N'pongo
29 October: Bamenda gives birth to Emba, a female infant, at Howletts Zoo
30 December: Motaba sires Buzandi, a male infant, at Melbourne Zoo, Australia

1992   7 March: Eighteenth gorilla birth at JWPT – a dead infant removed from Kishka by assisted delivery
March: Tatu sires female infant at Oklahoma Zoo, USA
3 April: Nandi found dead
15 August: N'gola sires Sitawi, a male infant at Zurich Zoo, Switzerland
4 May: Gorilla breeding complex visited by HRH The Princess Royal
16 September: Jambo found dead
28 September: Tatú's unnamed female infant dies at Oklahoma Zoo, USA
12 December: Sitawi dies at Zurich Zoo, Switzerland

1993   12 January: Kakinga sires Mbondi, a male infant, at Calgary Zoo, Canada
28 February: Kakinga sires N'tondo, a male infant, at Calgary Zoo, Canada
31 October: N'gola sires Tambo, a male infant at Zurich Zoo, Switzerland

BIBLIOGRAPHY

ALLCHURCH, A F (1980): Veterinary Report, Dodo J Jersey
Wildlife Preservation Trust 17: 106
ALLCHURCH, A F (1981): Veterinary Report, Dodo J Jersey   Wildlife
Preservation Trust:18: 94-97
ALLCHURCH, A F (1986): Nutritional Handbook of the JWPT
ASPINALL, J (1976): The Best of Friends, Macmillan
COUSINS, D (1990): The Magnificent Gorilla, The Book Guild
DU CHAILLU, P B (1861): Explorations and Adventures in Equatorial
Africa, John Murray
DURRELL, G M (1976): The Stationary Ark, Collins
DURRELL, G M (1991): The Ark's Anniversary, Collins
FOSSEY, D (1983): Gorillas in the Mist, Houghton Mifflin Co
HARCOURT, A (1987): Behaviour of Wild Gorillas and Their
Management in Captivity, International Zoo Yearbook 26: 248-55
JOHNSTONE-SCOTT, R A (1979): Shamba's Daughter Arrives   Early,
Help, Howletts and Port Lympne Newsletter
JOHNSTONE-SCOTT, R A (1982): Rwanda: Gorillas At Home, On the
Edge, JWPT Newsletter 43: 1-2
JOHNSTONE-SCOTT, R A (1984): An Everyday Story of a   Group of
Gorillas, The First Twenty-Five Year, JWPT
JOHNSTONE-SCOTT, R A (1984): Integration and   Management of
a Group of Lowland Gorilla at the Jersey Wildlife Preservation Trust,
Dodo, JWPT 25: 67-79
JOHNSTONE-SCOTT, R A (1988): The Potential for Establishing
Bachelor Groups of Western Lowland Gorillas Gorilla g. gorilla, Dodo,
JWPT 25: 61-6
JOHNSTONE-SCOTT, R A (1992): N'pongo Gives Birth, Gorilla
Gazette 6 (1): 1-4
JOHNSTONE-SCOTT, R A (1992): Farewell Nandi, On the Edge,
JWPT Newsletter 64: 7
JOHNSTONE-SCOTT, R A (1992): The Integration of Julia,
International Zoo News No 239 39/6: 18-26
JOHNSTONE-SCOTT, R A (1992): A Gorilla's Personal Space, On the
Edge JWPT Newsletter 64: 5-6

BIBLIOGRAPHY

JOHNSTONE-SCOTT, R A (1992): Jambo - End of an Era, Gorilla Gazette 6 (3): 4-5

LANG, E M (1964): Jambo - First Gorilla Raised by its Mother in Captivity!, National Geographic 125, No 3: 446-53

MALLINSON, J J C, COFFEY, P F and USHER-SMITH, J (1973): Maintenance, Breeding and Hand-Rearing of Lowland Gorilla Gorilla g. gorilla (Savage and Wyman 1847), at the Jersey Zoological Park, JWPT Annual Report 10: 5-28

MARVIN, N (1988): Assault on the Senses, BBC Wildlife 6 (12)

MURPHY, M F (1978): Gorillas are Vanishing, Intriguing Primates

PINCHIN, A (1993): Anthropomorphism: Science and Humanity, International Zoo News 239 (39/6): 3-6

PORTON, I, WHITE, M and BERRY, B (1992): Social Dynamics of a Bachelor Gorilla Group at the St Louis Zoo, International Conference Proc. Gorilla Workshop 1992, Milwaukee

SCHULTZ, A H (1950): Morphological Observations on Gorillas in The Anatomy of the Gorilla, The Henry Cushier Raven Memorial Volume: 227-53, Columbia University Press, New York

WILLOUGHBY, D P (1978); All About Gorillas, A S Barnes & Co Inc

FURTHER
INFORMATION

Papers published by the Jersey Wildlife Preservation Trust from 1962-92 are available upon request.

For further information about the organizations mentioned in this book, please write to:

The Jersey Wildlife Preservation Trust
  Les Augrès Manor, Trinity, Jersey JE3 5BF Channel Islands
  Tel: 0534 864666 Fax: 0534 865161
The Dian Fossey Gorilla Fund
  UK 110 Gloucester Avenue, London NW1 8JA
  Tel: 0171 483 2681 Fax: 0171 483 4541
John Aspinall's Gorilla Orphanage
  Donations to: Congo Project, Freepost DR 15,
  Hythe, Kent CT21 4PD
  Establised by The Howletts and Port Lympne Foundation
  Tel: 0303 264647
The Fauna and Flora Preservation Society and
  The Mountain Gorilla Project
  1 Kensington Gore, London SW7 2AR
  Tel: 0171 823 8899 Fax: 0171 823 9690
The World Wide Fund for Nature (WWF)
  WWF UK: Panda House, Weyside Park, Godalming,
  Surrey GU7 1XR
  Tel: 0483 426444 Fax: 0483 426409

SPONSORS

Within the zoological world, Jambo was recognized as a most significant individual. As the first male gorilla to be born in captivity, the first to be reared by its own mother and one of the most prolific breeding animals in captivity, his contribution to the saving of his species was immense. To visitors of Jersey Zoo, Jambo was the star attraction and the highlight of their day. To a wider television audience Jambo amazed millions of viewers around the world in his role as 'gentle giant' when he protected a young visitor who had fallen into his enclosure.

This magnificent creature also drew support for the sixty or more conservation breeding programmes at the headquarters of the Jersey Wildlife Preservation Trust, where the work of saving less charismatic species continues through the financial contribution of visitors to the zoo.

SAFE is the official appeal of the Jersey Wildlife Preservation Trust to save the same animals from extinction – in their countries of origin. Please write for further information to SAFE, Jersey Wildlife Preservation Trust, Les Augrès Manor, Trinity, Jersey, English Channel Islands, JE3 5BP.

When Jambo died, the Jersey Wildlife Preservation Trust established a memorial fund with a dual purpose. Its first objective was to help commemorate the life and times of this remarkable animal through the medium of this publication. The second aim was the commissioning of a full-size bronze of Jambo in appreciation of his service to the zoo and the species, *Gorilla g gorilla.*

The following names are those who responded to the appeal.

DONATIONS FOR JAMBO

The Lady Acton, Iowa, USA
Anonymous
M Arnold, London
M Archambault, Quebec, Canada
G Ashmore, Cardiff
P & D Audrain, Jersey
D & B Banks, Jersey
D Barnes, Jersey
S Baud, Bourg St Maurice, France
E Bayette, London
R & P Blake, Sheffield
W Briggs, Hastings, New Zealand
D Briginshaw, Isle of Wight
L & W Brown, Jersey
S Carswell & R Le Cocq de
  Dotteville, Jersey
B Clark, Dorset
I & A Clarke, Birmingham
L Colvin, Yorkshire
B Cook, London
S Cook, Sussex
A Cottrell, London
S Cowie, Jersey
K Cox, Co Sligo, Eire
P Crouch, Cheshire
M Cuthbert, Sussex
D Davies, Isle of Wight
H Dinsdale, Isle of Man
H Dorrell, Dorset
J Drinkall, Humberside
M Duffield, Yorkshire
P Dunham, Manchester
S Dunning, Cleveland
M Earnshaw, Leeds
G Evans, London
F & D Edmonds, Middlesex

G & X Foeldes, Bevaix,
  Switzerland
M & J Foster, Cleveland
C Gillespie, Glasgow
A Goddard & B Somerset,
  Somerset
J Greenfield, Dorset
M Groves, London
N Gwilt, Birmingham
L Hammond, Cleveland
In Memory of Mrs V Harrison,
  Jersey
S Hastings, Milton Keynes
R Henderson, Torinese, Italy
S Hopper, Devon
E Houghton, Somerset
J House, London
F Jenkins, Florida, USA
P Journeaux, Jersey
C Kamphuis, Rijswijk, The
  Netherlands
R Kibel, London
A. Kingston-Splatt, Hertfordshire
D Knott, Lancashire
M Louwers, Bristol
F Luce, Hertfordshire
W Lucy, Jersey
P & C Maindonald, Jersey
P Martin, Kent
S Mayes, Cheshire
J McElroy, Jersey
S & C Meyers, Derbyshire
K Nelissen, The Hague, Holland
B Nickson, Birmingham
S Norris, Essex
J O'Brien, Birmingham

Lady Oppenheimer, Jersey
M Papendieck, Germany
A Parker, Sussex
I Perry, Wiltshire
B Porter, Essex
M Powell, Ontario, Canada
C Powis, Sussex
G Quick
A Ollivier
G Price, Essex
J Ramm, Essex
P & F Reat, Norwich
E Reed, Chester
I Rigold, Quebec, Canada
A & F Rowcliffe
The Ruscoe Family, Alberta, Canada
M Russell, Kent
J Scott, Edinburgh
T & A Scott Warren, Jersey
S Selley, London
U Shah, Baroda, India
J Sibley, London
S Smith, Telford
B Stainton, Buckinghamshire

D Stapleton, Ontario, Canada
D & D Stocks, Queensland, Australia
G Tester, Hampshire
A & P Townsend, Oxford
K Tyler-Jepson, Jersey
J Tanner & C Ernest, Fife
M & E Tasker, Surrey
C & J Thomas, Middlesex
S Thomas, Jersey
N Troeger, St Moritz, Switzerland
In memory of Mrs Sheila Tubey
M Underwood, Jersey
I Vidakovits, Budapest, Hungary
I Vine, Dorset
J Watt, Montreal, Canada
M White, Missouri, USA
A Walker, Jersey
Wilkinson (Jersey) Limited, Jersey
A Williams, Victoria, Australia
D Williams, Cambridgeshire
The Winfield Family
W Yates, Como, Australia

PHOTOGRAPH ACKNOWLEDGMENTS

1. © Peter de Sousa
2. © *Sunday Mirror*
3. © Peter Studer
4. © Phillip Coffey
5. © Phillip Coffey
6. © *Jersey Evening Post*
7. © Phillip Coffey
8. © Phillip Coffey
9. © Phillip Coffey
10. © Phillip Coffey
11. © Phillip Coffey
12. © *Jersey Evening Post*
13. © Phillip Coffey
14. © Phillip Coffey
15. © *Jersey Evening Post*
16. © John Le Bas
17. © Phillip Coffey

18. © Phillip Coffey
19. © Phillip Coffey
20. © *Jersey Evening Post*
21. © Phillip Coffey
22. © *Jersey Evening Post*
23. © Zoological Society of Philadelphia
24. © *Jersey Evening Post*
25. © James Morgan
26. © John Le Bas
27. © *Jersey Evening Post*
28. © *Jersey Evening Post*
29. © *Jersey Evening Post*
30. © *Jersey Evening Post*
31. © *Jersey Evening Post*
32. © Jan Parks

The author and publisher and Durrell Wildlife Conservation Trust have made every effort to contact copyright holders for the photographs that appear in this book, and apologize to any whom they have been unable to trace. They will be glad to hear from anyone who may unwittingly have been overlooked.

INDEX